Acknowledgements

Authors

Nick Buenfeld BSc MSc PhD DIC CEng MICE MICT

Nick is a civil engineer and concrete technologist specialising in the durability of concrete structures. In 1987 he established the Concrete Durability Group at Imperial College London, a multi-disciplinary group of scientists and engineers aiming to advance understanding of deterioration processes and so develop more effective methods of design, assessment and repair of concrete structures. Since 2000 he has been Professor of Concrete Structures at Imperial. He has authored/co-authored over 150 publications in refereed journals and conference proceedings and has been a member of many technical committees producing guidance documents for industry. He has provided durability guidance to the designers and constructors of major projects around the world.

Ron Davies BSc MSc PhD

Ron has a first class BSc in chemistry and geology, an MSc in metallurgical engineering and a PhD, all from South Africa. He has 10 years of research experience, 20 years of industrial experience concerned with chemistry and corrosion and has authored over 30 publications. Since 2003 he has been working in the Concrete Durability Group on the development of sensors to measure air voids at the steel-concrete interface in hardened concrete.

Ali Karimi MEng PhD DIC

Ali has a first class MEng in civil engineering and a PhD in probabilistic assessment of reinforced concrete highway bridges, both from Imperial College London. After his PhD he worked on the analysis and design of offshore oil production facilities for two years at KBR. In 2003 he returned to Imperial to join the Concrete Durability Group as a research fellow. He specialises in probabilistic modelling and service life prediction.

Alan Gilbertson BSc MSc DIC FIStructE, FICE

After graduating from Birmingham University in 1967, Alan joined WS Atkins and spent the next 35 years involved as a designer and manager in a wide range of engineering projects. Since 2002 he has been a consultant to CIRIA and is the founding convenor of the Institution of Structural Engineers' study group on management of structures.

Project funders

The DTI have kindly agreed to the work produced for the DTI project (see *Foreword* and *Appendices*) being drawn upon for this guide and included on the accompanying CD. Additional funding has also been provided by CIRIA's core members and the following organisations:

The Highways Agency

Transport Scotland

Concrete Repairs Limited

CAPCIS

Industrial Advisory Group (IAG)

Members of the IAG for the DTI project (see *Foreword*) have contributed to this guide and in particular the contribution of Bill Martin (DTI) and Jonathan Wood (SSD Ltd) is acknowledged.

The industrial advisory group for this project was chaired by Alan Gilbertson (CIRIA). The following were active members of the group.

Javad Akhtar	Hyder
Brian Bell	Network Rail
David Bone	Royal Haskoning
John Broomfield	Consultant
John Cairns	Heriot-Watt University
Simon Claringbull	Eon-UK
John Drewett	Concrete Repairs Ltd
Alan Fairhurst	BNFL
Neil Henderson	Mott MacDonald
Gareth John	CAPCIS
Gareth Jones	STATS
Ted Kay	Concrete Society
Jon Knights	Halcrow
Neil Loudon	Highways Agency
Bill Martin	DTI
Alex Mastrogiacomo	Price Brothers (UK) Ltd
Stuart Matthews	BRE
Hazel McDonald	Transport Scotland
Bonny Umeadi	Greenwich University
Goncalo Vasconcelos	Transport for London
Jonathan Wood	Consultant

Foreword

In October 2004 the DTI awarded a 2 ½ year contract to a partnership between CIRIA and Imperial College to investigate the existing technology for automated monitoring of the deterioration of concrete structures and the models available to use the data obtained for the prediction of remaining service life.

The work was commissioned by the National Measurement System Directorate (NMSD) under the Materials Metrology Programme and was designed to sign-post industrial needs, opportunities and possibilities to guide industry and the DTI for future work in this technology area. The Industry Advisory Group formed by CIRIA to guide and inform the work was an important factor in the development of the project.

Reports on these two topics (monitoring and modelling) were submitted to the DTI in June 2007, together with a roadmap exploring the way forward and these reports inform and underpin this guide, and they are provided as a CD with the guide.

The subject area has proved to be extensive, young and dynamic with practitioners active throughout the world. The information gathered and the understanding gained is considerable. Some key points from the work are:

- there are many reasons to monitor structures including to compare the actual behaviour with that anticipated during design, to determine the rate of deterioration, to optimise the timing of maintenance and to warn of an impending failure
- automated monitoring offers potential benefits in relation to on-site testing, including reducing the need for access, identifying problems earlier and isolating climatic effects
- sensors and monitoring equipment are available to allow many important aspects of the behaviour of concrete structures to be automatically monitored including aspects of structural change (eg deflection, vibration, displacement, concrete and rebar strain and pre-stressing wire breaks), reinforcement corrosion (eg half cell potential, polarisation resistance and concrete resistivity), concrete temperature and moisture content
- a study of the case studies provided demonstrates that intelligent monitoring is a worldwide issue and the large number of providers of instrumentation listed demonstrates the depth and breadth of effort being devoted to it. There are examples of intelligent monitoring being successfully used to manage structures
- there are many potential obstacles to the adoption of monitoring. These include concerns over the accuracy, stability and durability of some types of sensor, the fact that very few service life models are able to utilise monitoring data and the difficulty of sustaining owner management systems over long periods. This guide makes the difficulties clear and provides access to information in support of decision-making
- with developments in wireless communications and sensor technologies and a better understanding by industry of what can be done, there is no doubt that future management of our built environment will increasingly benefit from the use of intelligent monitoring.

Contents

List of figures

List of tables

Intelligent monitoring CD

Attached to the inside back cover of this book you will find a CD-ROM containing three DTI reports:

1. ***Automated monitoring of the deterioration of concrete structures.***
2. ***Service life prediction of concrete structures based on automated monitoring.***
3. ***A roadmap for the development of intelligent monitoring of concrete structures.***

1 Introduction

1.1 BACKGROUND

Most of the developed world's infrastructure is built in concrete. The majority is required to remain in service for at least 50 years and structures such as major bridges, dams, heritage buildings and nuclear storage facilities are expected to have lives of over 100 years. In some cases owners expect their structures to continue in use almost indefinitely. For example, underground railways in city centres generally remain in use for as long as they can be kept in a safe condition, regardless of cost. With appropriate design, selection of materials and construction practice it is possible to produce concrete structures that will be adequately durable in most exposure environments. However there is a legacy of structures where deterioration is causing problems leading to excessive maintenance expenditure and in some cases premature replacement.

Concrete structures do deteriorate and the complex chemistry of cement, the use of steel reinforcement and the variety of exposure environments result in many often interacting degradation processes. For most structures deterioration is so slow that no early intervention is needed. However, eventually deterioration becomes more rapid and repair or replacement is required. This is costly in terms of the materials and labour used, the disruption to users and other social costs. Unexpected failures can have particularly severe financial, environmental and safety implications and may leave companies liable to prosecution and compensation claims.

As deterioration progresses, it becomes increasingly expensive to rectify. So it is important to identify deterioration early, determine its structural significance, and to monitor the structure so that a timely intervention is possible avoiding more serious problems. Often early protective and remedial action, if monitored, can substantially prolong the useful life of a structure. Monitoring is now primarily based on visual inspection. Risk assessment (often informal) is based mainly upon experience elsewhere, informed by such inspection. Sampling, testing and in situ monitoring are rare until problems become serious. They are usually driven by obvious concerns and not by developing problems that have not yet become visually evident. The limitations of this approach are particularly worrying when considering foundations and other inaccessible details where local severe deterioration can develop.

It is envisaged society will insist that the condition and risks for all significant structures are certified. This is likely to be demanded when some major high-profile structures have failed due to unseen deterioration. Those responsible for certification will require much more information to base their recommendations upon, such as the changing condition and strength of the structure and its likely performance in the future. Information on the changing behaviour of the structure will ideally come from sensors mounted on the structure providing real time condition information. Automated monitoring of this kind is already in place on a few structures, with measurements being taken via surface-mounted or embedded sensors and the data being transmitted to a remote office. To predict performance in the future from this data and to be able to estimate the remaining life of a structure requires a life prediction model.

Intelligent monitoring is automated monitoring which explicitly provides information on current condition and assists in predicting the remaining life of a component or structure

Currently there is active worldwide research in this area. This is aimed at developing and applying a wide range of sensors and at building models, which enable predictions to be made about future performance. In 2004 the National Measurement System Directorate of the Department of Trade and Industry (DTI) commissioned CIRIA and Imperial College to investigate the current state-of-art in the area of concrete construction. This work comprised a 30-month contract to investigate both sensors and how they are used and the available life prediction models and to prepare a state-of-the-art report including a road map for the future development of the technology in this area. The work was guided by an Industry Advisory Group (IAG) comprising of representatives of organisations responsible for owning and managing structures and those active in developing and applying the technology, and their names are listed on page iv. The three reports prepared for the DTI are enclosed with this guide on CD-Rom and should be referred to for further detailed information as necessary.

This guide is based upon the DTI project. It is designed to provide an introduction on the subject of intelligent monitoring and to assist users to access the wealth of information in the DTI reports. Users should be aware that intelligent monitoring is at an early stage of development and that its use will require specialist expertise both in initiating and managing the process and in carrying out the work. Engineers should actively look for and apply further developments in monitoring, which can be expected as outlined in the road map for the future development of this field.

1.2 HOW TO USE THIS GUIDE

This guide is written for all of those with an interest in monitoring including asset owners, consulting engineers, specialist contractors, suppliers and researchers.

Users of this guide may access information in the sections as follows:

1 The role of intelligent monitoring in the management of structures	Intelligent monitoring is one aspect of the management of structures. This section will assist in understanding how it fits into the wider picture.
2 Automated monitoring	This section explains the state-of-art of automated monitoring in 2007 with emphasis on techniques with a proven track record.
3 Prediction of remaining life based on monitoring data	Ideally the outputs from monitoring are fed into a model to provide guidance on the remaining life of a structure. This section describes the models available and how they may be used with monitoring data, exploring their attractions and limitations.
4 Case studies	An overview of the case studies in DTI Report 2 Appendix A2 to illustrate what has already been done.
5 Looking to the future	Here the guide explains what the future may hold and identifies areas meriting further research.

1.3 THE DTI REPORTS

This CIRIA guide is based on three reports produced during a DTI funded project, Intelligent monitoring of the deterioration of concrete structures. These reports are included on the CD attached to this CIRIA guide. They provide a greater level of detail than appropriate to include in this guide and are frequently referred to throughout the guide. If a discrepancy is found between the CIRIA guide and one of the DTI reports, the CIRIA guide should be taken as the more reliable source because the CIRIA guide was finished six months after the DTI reports and was more heavily scrutinised.

DTI report 1: Automated monitoring of the deterioration of concrete structures (Davies and Buenfeld, 2007)

This report presents the state-of-the-art in automated monitoring of the deterioration of concrete structures. It focuses on what is now practical, but also refers to methods under development. Considerable detail is provided on the sensors available to monitor:

- structural change (Chapter 3)
- reinforcing steel corrosion (Chapter 4)
- concrete moisture state and temperature (Chapter 5)
- concrete chemistry (Chapter 6)
- exposure environment (Chapter 7).

These chapters are sub-divided according to what is monitored. For each of the main methods, they highlight the measurement principle, advantages (in relation to competing techniques) and limitations, the equipment used and potential application areas. Chapter 3 of this CIRIA guide is based on this report.

The appendices contain a mass of useful information:

Appendix A1 provides datasheets for the different generic types of sensor and monitoring equipment together with a list of equipment manufacturers/suppliers and their contact details.

Appendix A2 presents 32 case studies reporting on experience in applying monitoring systems to various structures.

Appendix A3 lists journals and conferences that publish papers concerned with monitoring concrete structures.

DTI Report 2: Service life prediction of concrete structures based on automated monitoring (Karimi and Buenfeld, 2007)

This report reviews a large number of models for predicting the service life of concrete structures and discusses which are the most appropriate for use with data derived from automated monitoring. Models are empirical, analytical or numerical in nature and it is this characteristic that dictates the quantity and availability of the required input parameters. An overview is presented highlighting the main differences between modelling approaches, and probabilistic techniques are presented and discussed. The vast majority of service life models presented in the literature and used by industry have been developed independently of advances made in the field of automated monitoring. In many cases the role of intelligent monitoring is restricted to providing only one or two of the input variables and in a significant number of the models reviewed intelligent monitoring cannot take any active role in the assessment process. Chapter 4 of this CIRIA guide is based on this report and focuses on the models that are most appropriately used with monitoring data.

DTI Report 3: A roadmap for the development of intelligent monitoring of concrete structures, (Buenfeld, 2007)

This report presents a roadmap for the future development of the field of intelligent monitoring of concrete structures and is primarily based on the views of the Industrial Advisory Group for the DTI Project. It summarises the current state-of-the-art, presents a vision for the future and analyses what needs to be done to realise that vision. Chapter 6 of this CIRIA guide is largely based on this report.

2 The role of intelligent monitoring in the management of concrete structures

2.1 RESIDUAL LIFE PREDICTION

Monitoring systems may be applied to new or existing structures. For new structures the emphasis will often be on giving an early warning of significant deterioration taking place (for example, the chloride threshold level having been reached at the surface of the rebar). This is particularly important where inspection is difficult or impossible. For existing structures the emphasis will usually be on monitoring the rate of an already active deterioration process. The two cases, however, may be treated with the same basic approach once it is recognised that the common aim of monitoring should be to reliably indicate current condition and to enable estimation of the life of the structure and/or the time until repairs are required.

Structurally serious deterioration is often very localised, so it is essential to target monitoring at a representative sub set of critical areas. The estimated life of the structure should be based on consideration of the weakest links in the structural chain. Protection, remedial works and repairs often need to be focused on these local critical areas so that the life of the whole structure can be extended.

Figure 2.1 shows the relative roles of the various activities that may be used in assessing the residual life of a concrete structure.

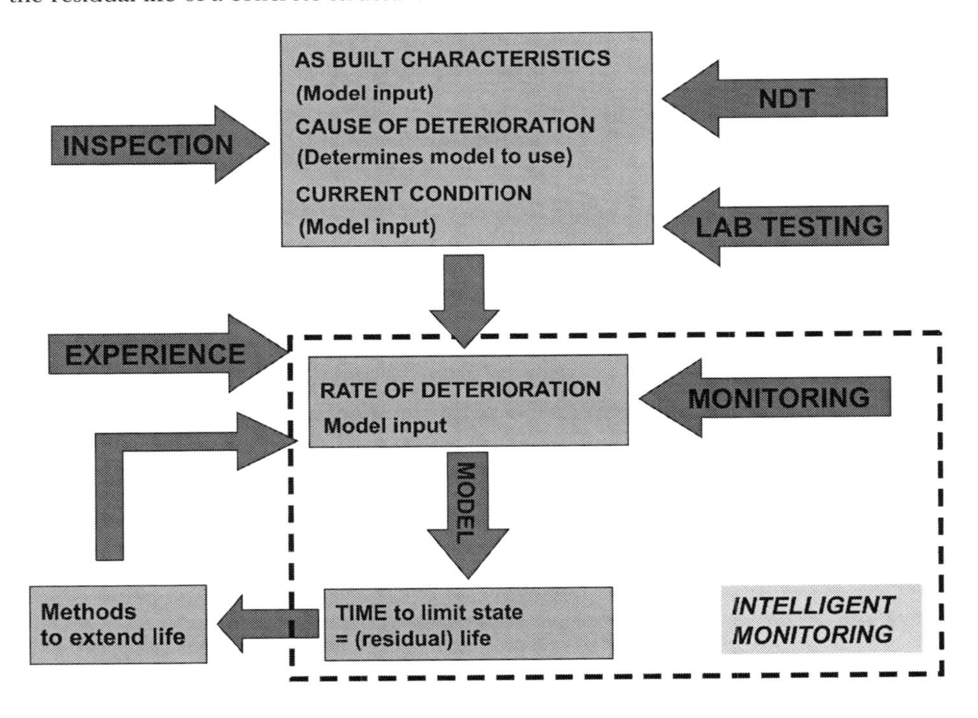

Figure 2.1 *The role of monitoring in the management of concrete structures*

For each identified sensitive area it is necessary to carry out non-destructive testing (NDT), sampling and testing to establish the deterioration trend to date. A preliminary extrapolation of time to stages of further deterioration can be made based on an appropriate model and experience. At each stage of deterioration the benefits of remedial action to slow deterioration or locally repair, replace or reconstruct damaged elements can be estimated. By appropriate monitoring for the conditions identified and with a flow of data from intelligent monitoring, the modelling for residual life prediction can be updated and refined so that risk and management options can be periodically reviewed.

The limit of acceptable deterioration needs to be defined, when a limit state of inadequate factor of safety or reliability is reached at which the structure is beyond economic repair. This limit state against collapse or serviceability will correspond to those considered in design and/or a particular requirement of the client. The time to reach this limit state for a particular part of the structure is its residual life. When any critical part of a structure reaches this state, the whole structure has reached the end of its residual life. Using deterioration and strength modelling enables the benefits of a range of different remedial measures to be compared relative to lifetime costs over the time of the extended residual life.

2.2 ASSESSMENT OF CURRENT CONDITION AND CAUSE OF DETERIORATION

Before undertaking automated monitoring, or trying to predict residual life, it is necessary to establish the starting condition of the structure and the potential deterioration mechanisms. For a new structure, before construction, this will involve analysing the range of exposure environment of sensitive details to assess potentially important deterioration mechanisms, reviewing the specification of materials and associated testing and site quality control procedures. This should always be reviewed during construction and at the end of the construction maintenance period, to determine cover variation, actual exposure conditions, construction defects, cracking, poor compaction adjacent to joints, deflections adversely affecting drainage and other features likely to adversely affect durability. From this the fixed parameters for modelling (eg variability of cover to reinforcement, variability of concrete properties) can be established. Similarly variable properties that can change or be changed over the life of the structure can be established (eg drainage conditions sensitive to creep and blockage, failure of the sealing of expansion joints).

For an existing structure the datum as-built condition needs to be determined based on a detailed visual inspection for all apparent features likely to adversely affect durability and some laboratory testing of concrete samples cut from the structure and some on-site non-destructive testing. The drawings and structure also need reviewing to identify where there are structurally sensitive details or hidden vulnerable details that cannot be inspected. The comparison of as-built with aged condition enables preliminary estimates of deterioration trends to be extrapolated.

Provision of guidance on these activities is beyond the scope of this report and is already covered by several guidance documents. For example *Testing of concrete structures* (Bungey and Millard, 1996), *Manual of concrete practice* (ACI, (NDT) 2003), *Guide to testing and monitoring the durability of concrete structures* (Concrete Bridge Development Group, 2002) and *Diagnosis of deterioration in concrete structures* (Concrete Society, 2000). A longer list is provided in Sections 2.1.2 and 2.3.2 of DTI Report 1.

2.3 DEFINITION OF LIMIT STATE(S)

Once the primary cause of deterioration is established, the critical *limit state(s)* should be defined. A *limit state* is a condition which when reached requires a *planned intervention*. This intervention could be:

- demolishing and replacing the structure
- carrying out major repairs (eg removing and recasting concrete)
- carrying out minor repairs (eg patch repairs or application of a surface coating)
- applying cathodic protection
- increasing the amount of monitoring.

The planned intervention will depend on, among other factors, the type of structure and the main deterioration mechanism(s). For example, the planned intervention for a maritime jetty subject to chloride-induced rebar corrosion could be demolition and replacement. In contrast, the planned intervention for a tall building subject to carbonation-induced rebar corrosion could be application of a carbonation-resisting surface treatment to the concrete, thereby pre-empting the hazard of spalling concrete falling from the structure. Clearly the nature of the planned intervention will be the major factor in determining the limit state. For example, limit states may be associated with:

- loss of function (eg water leakage from a water retaining structure exceeding a certain rate)
- loss of strength (eg a percentage loss in compressive strength of an RC column)
- degradation in other aspects of structural behaviour (eg midspan deflection of an RC beam exceeding a certain value)
- safety hazard (eg concrete falling from a building)
- corrosion initiation (eg a certain percentage of rebar starting to corrode, or carbonation reaching a certain depth)
- aesthetics (eg cracks exceeding a certain width and becoming visible).

The critical serviceability and ultimate limit states identified for the most common deterioration processes are presented in Table 2.1. Depending on the type of structure under consideration, the end of the service life may be defined as the attainment of any of these limit states. Although the underlying degradation mechanisms of sulphate attack, freeze-thaw attack and alkali-aggregate reaction vary considerably, the resulting mechanical damage they inflict on concrete is similar in nature. So a common set of limit states are assigned to these three deterioration processes (see Section 4.5.2 for more detail).

Table 2.1 *Common deterioration processes and corresponding critical limit states*

<table>
<tr><th>Deterioration mechanism</th><th>Serviceability limit states</th><th>Ultimate limit states</th></tr>
<tr><td>Reinforcement corrosion</td><td>□ initiation of rebar corrosion
□ full depth cracking of concrete cover
□ excessive crack widths
□ spalling*
□ excessive deflections.</td><td>□ flexural failure (yielding of steel, crushing of concrete)
□ shear failure
□ anchorage failure.</td></tr>
<tr><td>Sulphate attack</td><td rowspan="3">□ formation of an extensive network of internal micro-cracks
□ full depth cracking of concrete cover
□ spalling*
□ excessive distortion.</td><td rowspan="3">□ degradation of mechanical properties of concrete (eg loss of compressive strength, loss of rigidity).</td></tr>
<tr><td>Freeze-thaw attack</td></tr>
<tr><td>Alkali-aggregate reaction</td></tr>
</table>

Note:

* If spalling of concrete endangers human life it should be categorised as an ultimate limit state.

2.4 ASSESSMENT OF RATE OF DETERIORATION

Predicting future condition requires knowledge of the rate of deterioration. If a large body of information exists concerning the performance of similar concrete in comparable exposure environments, it may be possible to estimate the rate of deterioration, for example the rate of loss of cross-section of rebars in carbonated concrete. But this is not usually possible.

If access to the structure is not difficult, if the deterioration process of concern can be monitored from the concrete surface and if the measurements are not too sensitive to the prevailing environmental conditions, then periodic on-site testing may be an appropriate means of acquiring rate of deterioration information.

At present by far the most widely practised form of monitoring of concrete structures is visual inspection. It is during visual inspections that signs of degradation, for example concrete cracking or surface deposits, are most likely to be observed. Even if an automated monitoring system is installed, visual inspection should be carried out wherever possible. This is because visual inspection is relatively inexpensive and allows a larger area of concrete surface to be scanned than is possible with automated monitoring. It should be recognised that visual inspection is confined to the accessible surface of a structure. It is not usually practical to visually inspect the buried or clad parts of a structure. Also, rebar corrosion is the most widespread and costly deterioration mechanism and by the time evidence of corrosion is apparent at the concrete surface, the level of corrosion usually requires fairly major repairs.

There are several major benefits of automated monitoring in relation to on-site testing, as outlined below.

1 *The influence of climatic conditions can be isolated.* Many of the measurements of interest are influenced by the climatic conditions at, or shortly before, the time that the measurement is taken. For example, temperature influences concrete resistivity and relative humidity influences half-cell potential. The seasonal variations in these parameters may completely change the conclusions drawn from them. Consequently, single time readings can be misleading. Automated monitoring allows measurements to be made every day, or indeed many times each day, so that such influences may be determined and isolated more effectively.

2 *The need for access is reduced.* Regular measurements may be made even if the structure, or component, is difficult to gain access to. This may be due to:

- geographic location (eg an offshore structure)
- local position (eg a buried foundation or the top of a bridge pier)
- function (eg a nuclear pressure vessel)
- a requirement not to take the structure out of service (eg a motorway bridge deck or a pipeline).

3 *Measurements may be made at the depth of interest.* On-site, non-destructive testing usually involves taking measurements at the surface of the concrete. In some cases this is too far from the area of interest to provide reliable data. With automated monitoring sensors can be embedded at the location of interest, particularly if they are installed at the time of construction. For example, this allows strain gauges to be attached to rebar and corrosion sensors to be placed near to the rebar of interest, even if this is at the bottom of a deep pile or near the centre of a thick concrete element. At present the sensors to monitor most properties must be hardwired to the instrumentation taking and recording the measurement. This often limits the number of sensors deployed. Note that major developments in wireless communications and related sensor technology mean that wireless sensors for embedding in concrete are likely to be widely available within the next five years. Wireless sensors for geotechnical monitoring have already been available for a few years.

4 *Initiation of deterioration is identified earlier.* Some deterioration processes take many years to start (initiation phase) and then lead to rapid deterioration (propagation phase), for example, chloride-induced corrosion arising from sea-water penetration. In such cases it is usually important to identify, as early as possible, that the propagation phase has started so that appropriate remedial measures may be implemented (a planned intervention). Automatic monitoring will identify that the propagation phase has started much earlier than on-site, non-destructive testing carried out every, say, five or 10 years.

Many of the traditional on-site non-destructive test methods that are now used to inspect concrete structures can be adapted for remote monitoring of properties/behaviour, such as strain, displacement, acoustic emission, vibration, steel potential and corrosion rate, concrete resistivity, temperature, humidity/moisture content, and exposure condition factors such as weather, groundwater and air composition.

3 Automated monitoring

3.1 INTRODUCTION

This chapter presents the state-of-the-art of *automated monitoring*. In many cases the monitoring methods described are not being used now for *intelligent monitoring*, because predictive models (covered in Chapter 4) are not available to use the monitoring data that they produce. Previous monitoring work on all major types of concrete structure has been taken into account including examples of the monitoring of buildings, bridges, foundations, pavement, dams, tunnels, and pipelines as well as the external environment itself including soil, air and water. Monitoring will often be applied to a component of a structure (for example, the area around a joint or bridge bearing) rather than an entire structure. The term *structure* is used for simplicity, but should be interpreted as meaning *structure* or *component*. All forms of structural concrete are considered, plain concrete, reinforced concrete and pre-stressed concrete. The monitoring approaches discussed are applicable to both new and existing structures, although the method of installation of sensors and treatment of the results may differ between them, and these differences are highlighted. All common exposure environments including those leading to carbonation-induced corrosion, chloride-induced corrosion, sulphate attack (in its various forms), freeze/thaw damage, alkali-aggregate reaction, leaching and abrasion are considered. Deterioration is interpreted in its widest sense to include loss of structural capacity, spalling, cracking, rebar corrosion and micro-structural and chemical changes.

Table 3.1 lists the properties/behaviour that it would be beneficial to monitor remotely and what is now feasible. Cross references are provided to later sections of the guide where specific methods are described in detail.

Section 3.2 gathers together key issues to be taken into account when considering, specifying or commissioning a monitoring system.

Sections 3.3-3.7 describe the sensors/techniques available, or under development, for monitoring structural change, reinforcing steel corrosion, concrete temperature, concrete moisture state and concrete chemistry respectively. These sections briefly describe the sensors, describing what can be measured, the principle of operation, the main advantages and disadvantages and example applications. The reader is referred to Chapters 3 to 6 of DTI Report 1 for more detail: Chapter 3 Structural change, Chapter 4 Reinforcing steel corrosion, Chapter 5 Concrete moisture state and temperature, Chapter 6 Concrete chemistry. In addition, Appendix A1.1 of DTI Report 1 provides datasheets giving key information on the main sensor types and Appendix A1.2 provides information on manufacturers/suppliers of sensors.

Ideally quantitative information would be presented on the resolution, accuracy, service life, etc for each of the sensor types mentioned in a consistent format. This is possible for sensors that have been used, in their current form, for many years. However, most of the sensors available do not have such an extensive track record and this information is not available, or, if it is, it has not been independently verified.

Section 3.8 provides an overview of monitoring the exposure environment. This is included because residual life prediction models sometimes require environment exposure variable inputs which may vary with time. Furthermore, the field of environmental monitoring is more developed than that of monitoring concrete structures and so there are transferable insights on offer.

Section 3.9 covers the equipment downstream of the sensors for data logging, transmission and computer evaluation.

Table 3.1 ***Properties/behaviour that it would be beneficial to monitor remotely and what is now feasible***

	Structural change	Rebar corrosion	Moisture state and temperature	Chemistry
RC/PSC section	Section strength	Chloride threshold level		
	Element deflection (Section 3.3.3)			
	Vibration (Section 3.3.6)			
Joints and cracks	Displacement (Section 3.3.3)			
Concrete	Concrete stress (Section 3.3.4)	Concrete resistivity (Section 3.4.3)	Temperature (Section 3.5)	Total chloride content
	Concrete strain (Section 3.3.2)	See chemistry column re chlorides, pH and nitrite	Moisture state (Section 3.6)	Free chloride content (Section 3.7.2)
	Cracking (Section 3.3.3)			pH (Section 3.7.3)
	Young's modulus			Sulphate content
				Alkali silicate gel content
				Nitrite content
Steel	Rebar strain (Section 3.3.2)	Half-cell potential (Section 3.4.2)		
	Rebar stress	Galvanic current (Section 3.4.4)		
	Cable stress	Polarisation resistance (Section 3.4.5)		
	Wire breaks (Section 3.3.5)	Cumulative corrosion (Section 3.4.6)		
		Electrochemical noise (Section 3.4.7)		
External environment	Earthquake (Section 3.8.4)	Stray currents in soil (Section 3.8.2)	Water/soil temperature, pressure (Section 3.8.2)	Water/groundwater pH, chloride and sulphate concentration, redox potential (Section 3.8.2)
			Air temperature, humidity, rainfall, wind (Section 3.8.3)	Air gaseous composition (Section 3.8.3)

Note
Shading: well proven methodology for automated monitoring (dark grey), currently possible, but not well proven (light grey), not currently possible (no shading).

3.2 PLANNING AND OPERATING A MONITORING SYSTEM

3.2.1 Purpose of monitoring

It is essential to be clear about the purpose of monitoring and the specific management uncertainties it will reduce before designing and commissioning a monitoring system. You need to be clear on *what*, *where* and *when* you will need to monitor to identify developing trends in structure behaviour. The relationship of what you monitor to the expected normal behaviour of the structure and to the abnormalities in behaviour you are seeking to quantify needs to be calibrated relative to your predictions of expected behaviour before anything is fitted. A good start is to apply the philosophy described in Chapter 2 for the structure concerned.

It is essential to understand the environments to which different parts of the structure and the instrumentation are exposed. The environment not only creates the conditions for deterioration, but will also change the calibration of your instrumentation. It also controls the normal cycles of thermal and shrinkage movement in the concrete which you will need to differentiate from the phenomenon you are monitoring. It is important to decide on the planned intervention, to define the associated critical limit state and to be clear about the models that will be used to predict both the structural responses and the time until the limit will be reached.

3.2.2 Variables measured

The phenomena to be monitored need to be closely related to the structural and service life models. It is usually advisable to monitor several aspects of behaviour at a representative range of locations to provide extra insight and to give confidence in the results. The benefits of monitoring should be ascertained for early indication of deterioration (eg chemical changes) or the consequential structural changes, or both.

Instrumentation should cover secondary factors that will influence the primary measurements. The most common example of this is compensating for the effects of temperature variation on strains and the effects of differential temperatures on the structure overall, between the surface and interior of members and between the gauge location (perhaps on the surface) and the mean temperature of the member. The seasonal wetting and drying strains of concrete can also be significant and need to be considered in the positioning of gauges and in monitoring secondary changes in moisture levels. The optimal approach will vary according to what is being measured and the type of sensor being used. One approach is to take reference measurements in locations and directions of negligible structural strain for which only temperature and moisture influence the result. Another is to measure temperature and correct for its effects during the analysis of the results. Consideration should be given to monitoring other aspects of the exposure environment. Sometimes this will be necessary to provide input data for a model. On other occasions it will be necessary to help explain variations in the measurements.

3.2.3 Sensor/equipment selection

Most of this chapter is dedicated to giving the best available information to guide the selection of sensors and other monitoring equipment. This section highlights some key issues that may apply whatever the application. The objective has been to provide information for a working engineer developing a practical approach to a monitoring opportunity in managing a real structure.

In this guide we have reviewed and aim to guide the engineer to fuller sources of information on proven techniques and recent innovations, which may become widely accepted over the next five to 10 years. There are a range of sensors that are at the speculative experimental stage or remain of little practical use despite years of trials. These are only briefly referred to in this guide, but have been explained in DTI Report 1.

Table 3.1 presented the properties/behaviour that can be remotely monitored, without much reference to the techniques involved. Table 3.2 lists the main techniques, broken down into gauge type where appropriate, and classifies each according to how widely they have been used and how effective they are for automated monitoring. A technique is indicated as *widely used* (Y) if it appears regularly in the automated monitoring case studies reported in the literature. Some techniques are widely used, but not for automated monitoring (for example the mechanical strain gauge) and so are indicated as N. A technique is indicated as *effective* (Y) if it is has been clearly demonstrated to be effective for certain automated monitoring applications. An effective technique gives accurate measurements over a period of many years, without being very difficult or very expensive to implement. "–" indicates that insufficient information is available to decide whether a technique is effective or not. Clearly this table is only indicative, relates to the present time (2007) and does not capture many of the issues that need to be considered when choosing a technique. The following sections on the different techniques provide more information and DTI Report 1 provides a greater level of detail.

Deciding between well proven sensors and those with little track record, but which seem to be more informative, is a common dilemma due to the rapidly developing nature of some of the technologies involved. It is prudent to adopt a combination of the old and the new. A particular example is the recent rapid development of wireless communications technologies now used in wireless sensors.

Reinforced concrete buildings are usually required to remain in service for at least 50 years. In the UK highway bridges have a design life of 120 years and special structures sometimes have much longer design lives. These lives are far longer than the track records of any of the sensors that we would want to consider using and far longer than the guarantees that suppliers will offer on their equipment. One approach is to design the monitoring system so that the components can be replaced, either when they fail, or at a particular time. A possible approach for new structures, although there are very few examples of this having been done in practice, is to detail them so that a monitoring system can be installed at a later date, nearer the time when deterioration is expected.

This highlights the dilemma between using surface mounted and embedded sensors. Embedded sensors may be placed nearer to the rebar (important for corrosion sensors) and are less readily vandalised. However, surface mounted sensors are more easily replaced and are less likely to be damaged during concrete construction. For the monitoring of existing structures, surface mounted sensors also avoid the problems associated with using an embedment mortar that will inevitably be chemically and micro-structurally different to surrounding concrete, so that early sensor readings will be associated with the mortar not the surrounding concrete.

Table 3.2 *The degree of use and effectiveness of the main monitoring techniques*

		Widely used?	Effective?
Structural change (Section 3.3)	Strain (Section 3.3.2)		
	Mechanical strain gauge	N	Y
	Electrical resistance strain gauge	Y	Y
	Vibrating wire strain gauge	Y	Y
	Optical fibre strain gauge		Y
	Crack/displacement (Section 3.3.3)		
	Mechanical gauge	N	Y
	Inductive displacement transducer	Y	Y
	Electrical resistance crack gauge	N	–
	Electrolytic tilt sensor	Y	Y
	Stress (Section 3.3.4)	N	Y
	Acoustics (Section 3.3.5)		
	Acoustic emission	N	–
	Acoustic monitoring	Y	Y
	Acceleration/vibration (Section 3.3.6)	Y	Y
Rebar corrosion (Section 3.4)	Half cell potential (Section 3.4.2)	Y	–
	Concrete resistivity (Section 3.4.3)	Y	Y
	Galvanic current (Section 3.4.4)	Y	–
	Linear polarisation resistance (Section 3.4.5)	Y	–
	Electrical resistance (Section 3.4.6)	N	–
	Electrochemical noise (Section 3.4.7)	N	N
Concrete temperature (Section 3.5)	Thermocouples (Section 3.5.2)	Y	Y
	Resistance thermometers (Section 3.5.3)	Y	Y
	Thermistors (Section 3.5.4)	N	Y
	Fibre optic sensors (Section 3.5.5)	N	–
Concrete moisture state (Section 3.6)	Humidity (Section 3.6.2)		
	Capacitive sensor	N	–
	Dew point sensor	N	–
	Wood/brick resistance sensor	N	–
	Fibre optic sensor	N	N
	Electrical resistivity (Section 3.6.3)	Y	Y
Concrete chemistry (Section 3.7)	Chloride (Section 3.7.2)	N	N
	pH (Section 3.7.3)	N	N
Exposure environment (Section 3.8)	Water and soil (Section 3.8.2)	Y	Y
	Air (Section 3.8.3)	Y	Y
	Earthquake (Section 3.8.4)	Y	Y

3.2.4 Number, location and installation of sensors

The number and location of sensors need to be closely related to the structural and service life models being used. Extra sensors should be fitted to provide support for failing sensors. The sensors and any associated periodic sampling of the structure to provide checks on sensor performance need to quantify the inherent variability from the heterogeneity of concrete and the uncertainties of workmanship.

When deciding where to locate sensors, it is important to identify the areas that are likely to deteriorate first. These tend to be:

- where wetting and drying and local concentration of chlorides or sulphates can accelerate deterioration
- corners and joints (that suffer from biaxial penetration and locally poor compaction)
- where cracking is possible (both structural and non-structural)
- where the concrete is likely to be most penetrable (eg the top of a pour and where congestion of reinforcement makes compaction difficult).

Thought should also be given to monitoring representative locations in the larger areas expected to deteriorate less rapidly. The importance of spatial variability of deterioration mechanisms and means of accounting for this variability in service life prediction are discussed in Section 4.6.5.

Sensors should be located so as to minimise their influence on the effects being monitored. For example, embedded rebar corrosion sensors should not create an easy path for chloride penetration. Where feasible, sensors should be installed from behind the face being monitored. In the future, the use of wireless sensors will mitigate this problem.

Great care should be taken in the installation of embedded sensors to minimise the risk of the mortar not bonding well with the surrounding concrete or experiencing shrinkage cracking. In both cases this would create an easy path for environmental penetration. When sensors show readings giving rise to concern it is essential to check for these anomalies by sampling into the surrounding concrete.

3.2.5 Data management

Considerable flexibility in managing data from sensors is now possible through technological advances in communications and computers. Newer sensors have built-in data logging and in some cases data transmission facilities. The question of wired versus wireless depends on the given situation, but wireless systems are very versatile and are likely to replace many wired monitoring systems in the future.

The monitoring of civil engineering structures is a long-term exercise, and once sensitivity of measurements to daily thermal effects has been established there is generally no need to accumulate data on a more frequent basis than perhaps one or two data sets per day. Less frequent data accumulation increases battery life and sensors can be pre-programmed to sleep for set periods to reduce power consumption.

Data transmitted back to a central computer is now routinely analysed automatically in real time, with the degree of analysis depending on the sophistication of the software. Experienced staff are necessary to interpret and keep track of the monitoring results. Responsibility for managing the results depends on the approach adopted. Sometimes the installation company takes on the responsibility and sends results with analysis and recommendations continuously to the client. This avoids the client having to employ dedicated and experienced staff, but the approach adopted often depends on cost considerations.

See Section 3.9 for a more detailed treatment of data management.

3.2.6 Maintenance

The periodic inspection and maintenance of the entire monitoring system is important if continuous and reliable results are to be expected. This involves inspection of external sensors and any cabling for environmental damage (for example from falling debris, vandalism, or lightning) to include replacement of damaged, external sensors.

The sensors need to be calibrated periodically to ensure that they provide realistic results. This can be carried out on-site or in some cases remotely. Infrequent calibration is adequate because unusual trends of particular sensors relative to adjacent sensors will indicate a faulty sensor. Embedded sensors in most cases cannot be calibrated and seldom can be replaced if faulty, and an expected redundancy rate should be built into the design of the monitoring system. In planning the overall system, consideration should be given to how sampling checks (eg of chloride profiles, or corrosion potentials) adjacent to sensors might be carried out if unusual trends develop.

3.2.7 Health and safety

Monitoring systems are usually designed so that they do not interfere with wireless or other electrically operated equipment on the structure being monitored. An excellent example of the design precautions necessary is the installation and operation of a tunnel monitoring system reported by Aylott *et al*, 2003. It is equally important to be aware of the potential interference to instrumentation in electrically hostile conditions (eg adjacent to railways).

3.2.8 Other sources of information

Intelligent monitoring of the deterioration of concrete structures is a multi-disciplinary and rapidly developing field. Expert guidance should be sought where possible. Sensor and equipment manufacturers and their contact details (including website information) are listed in Appendix A1.2 of DTI Report 1 by product type. Useful sources of information on sensor and monitoring system manufacturers, structural monitoring reports and developments can be found in Appendix A3 of DTI Report 1, which lists websites, journals and conference proceedings relevant to monitoring concrete structures.

3.3 STRUCTURAL CHANGE

3.3.1 Introduction

A concrete structure may experience structural damage during its life caused by in-service loading and/or exposure to the environment. This section concerns the monitoring of structural changes manifested by changes in strain (Section 3.3.2), cracking/displacement (Section 3.3.3), stress (Section 3.3.4), acoustic emission (Section 3.3.5) or acceleration/vibration (Section 3.3.6). Methods under development are described in Section 3.3.7. Monitoring of rebar corrosion and chemical changes, which if advanced may cause structural changes, are covered in Sections 3.4 and 3.7

respectively. Brief reference is made to data logging instrumentation required for storing and transmitting the signal by cable or telemetry to a remote computer. Data loggers are standard instrumentation that can accept and transmit an electrical signal, and may also perform control functions such as switching a sensor on or off at pre-set intervals to take a reading or to conserve battery power. More detailed information on data logging and transmission systems is provided in Section 3.9.

3.3.2 Strain

3.3.2.1 *General*

A distinction is made in this guide between strain and displacement monitoring. So unless otherwise indicated *strain* means the change in length per unit length (more accurately known as *linear strain*), as opposed to volume or shear strain. Strain monitoring generally requires the measurement of a dimensional change of less than a few millimetres over a gauge length of several centimetres. In contrast, *displacement* refers to a movement, where absolute, rather than fractional, length change is of interest (for example, the opening of an expansion joint) and may involve a movement of up to several centimetres. Displacement monitoring is covered in Section 3.3.3.

Strain is defined as fractional change per unit length, usually expressed as micro-strain. Various sensor types are used in gauges for measuring strain in concrete structures based on mechanical, electrical or acoustic principles. These sensors convert measured behaviour into an electrical signal and can be used for automated monitoring. Where cracking occurs, crack or displacement gauges are more appropriately used (see Section 3.3.3).

The ideal strain gauge shows a direct relationship with the degree of deformation of the surface to which it is attached or embedded. In practice, however, other variables influence the result such as temperature, the adhesive bond holding the sensor to the structure, and stability of the sensor material. A fundamental property of a strain gauge is the sensitivity to strain, expressed quantitatively as the gauge factor (GF), the fractional change in output to the fractional change in length (strain).

Measuring strain in an inhomogeneous material such as concrete requires the selection of a strain gauge of sufficient gauge length to span several pieces of aggregate to measure the representative strain in the structure. This avoids measuring local strains that may be confined to the cement paste-aggregate interface.

Manufacturers also provide useful information and guidance on sensor and gauge selection (see list of equipment manufacturers in Appendix A1.2 of DTI Report 1).

3.3.2.2 *Mechanical strain gauge*

Mechanical strain gauges involve a spring lever system. This type of gauge is used for measuring strain in structures, but is more appropriately applied to displacement and crack monitoring (Section 3.3.3). The gauge is not normally left in place on the structure. When a measurement is to be taken, the gauge is placed on two pins rigidly fixed to the structure, a measurement taken and the gauge then removed. Calibration is made at the same time cancelling out any temperature effects.

Both dial and digital gauge readouts are available in the widely used DEMEC strain gauge (Mayes Instruments, UK). DEMEC strain gauges are available in gauge lengths from 50 to 200 mm, and can measure strain movements up to 5 mm. Gauge sensitivity varies from 2 to 20 micro-strain.

It is possible to leave the digital gauge in place on a structure when adequately protected from the elements, and monitor gauge changes remotely via suitable instrumentation (a temperature sensor would also be needed). Mitutoyo (Japan) provide instrumentation to accept a signal from the gauge for automated monitoring.

3.3.2.3 *Electrical resistance strain gauge*

This is the most widely used type of strain gauge. It measures the change in electrical resistance of a metal foil or wire sensor when deformed. For a given current, the potential of a foil or wire will change as it is stretched or compressed, in proportion to the strain. Sensitive instrumentation is required to measure the resistance change accurately, and usually comprises a Wheatstone bridge circuit, with the output voltage signal amplified by electronics.

The majority of strain gauges in use today for monitoring concrete structures are the foil type, which consists of a thin metal foil (typically 0.010 mm thick) arranged in the form of a grid pattern (eg Figure 3.1), and mounted on a thin plastic backing (the carrier). The carrier is attached directly to the concrete structure using a thin layer of adhesive, which also serves as an insulator. They are essentially printed circuits in which the metal has been removed by photo-etching to form a grid pattern. The grid pattern maximises the length of foil subject to strain in the parallel direction. The cross-sectional area of the grid is minimised to reduce the effects of strain in the lateral direction.

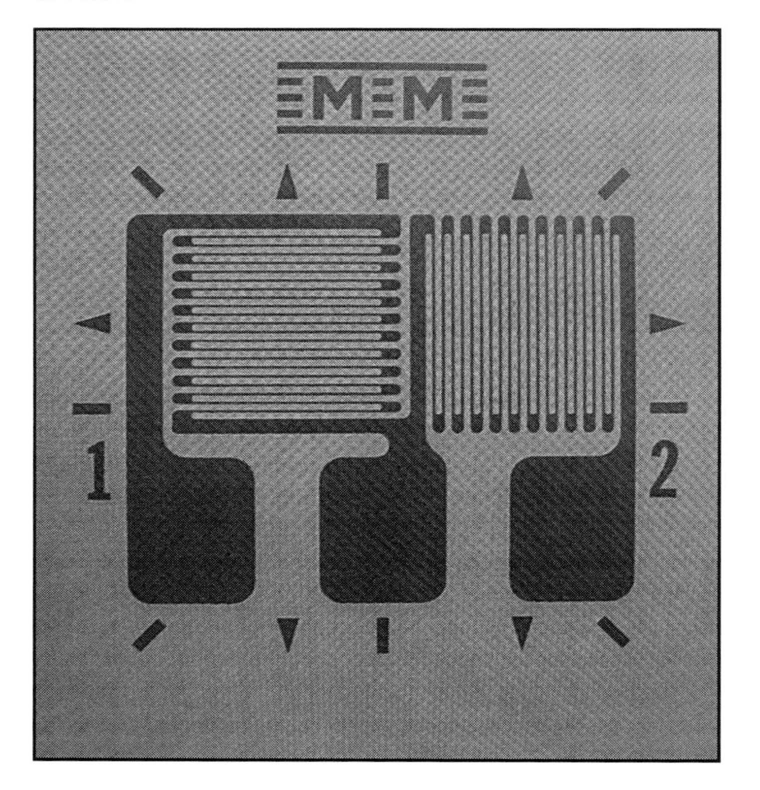

Figure 3.1 *Strain gauge grid (courtesy Vishay)*

Strain gauges are available in a variety of designs for measuring strain in one direction, suited to measuring strain along the length of a reinforcing bar, or in several directions for use on flat concrete surfaces or for embedding in concrete. Surface mounted strain gauges are the typical foil type with a plastic backing. Embedded strain gauges consist of wire or foil encapsulated in resin or polymer concrete with a rough surface to provide good attachment to the concrete (eg Figure 3.2).

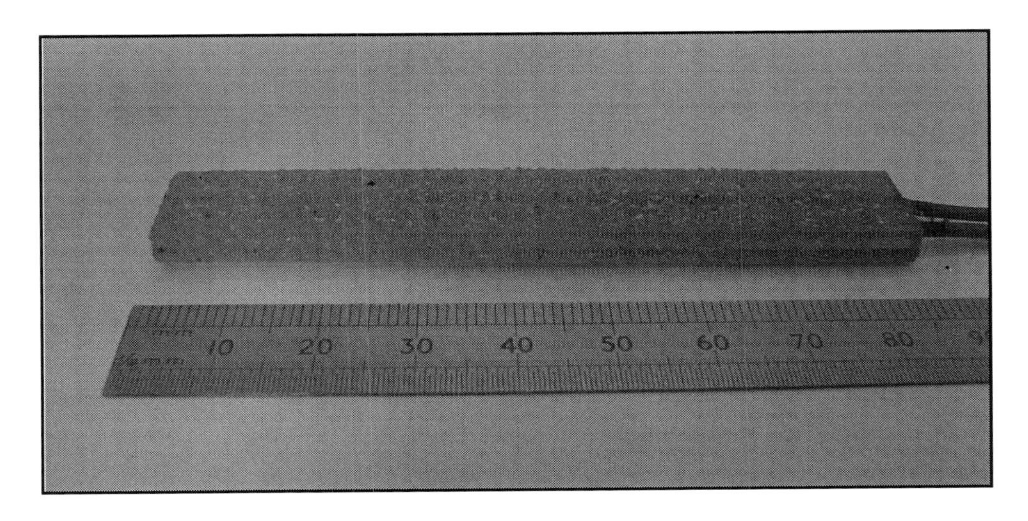

Figure 3.2 *Embeddable strain gauge*

The mounting and protection of foil strain gauges is critical. Epoxy resin is usually used to glue the gauge to the structure and to protect the gauge from moisture. The correct type of resin specified by the supplier should be used because some epoxy resins are prone to creep. Cracking of the resin in the long-term is a limitation.

Most materials are sensitive to temperature variation, and tend to change their resistance with age. This is not a problem for monitoring short-term changes, but for long-term monitoring temperature and drift compensation should be considered. The most common metals used for strain gauge sensors are copper-nickel and nickel-chromium alloys. Constantan (60 per cent copper and 40 per cent nickel), the most widely used metal, is relatively insensitive to temperature changes in the range -30 to 193°C, but nickel-chromium alloys have a large temperature coefficient. Strain gauge manufacturers attempt to minimise sensitivity to temperature using approaches such as controlling the processing of the sensor material, using a self-compensating gauge, incorporating a thermocouple with the sensor or by using two strain gauges in the bridge circuit, one the sensing gauge, the other a dummy gauge orientated at right angles to the first.

3.3.2.4 *Vibrating wire (acoustic) strain gauge*

A vibrating wire strain gauge operates on the principle that a tensioned wire vibrates at a frequency that is proportional to the strain in the wire when plucked. The wire is made from high tensile strength, heat treated and tempered steel, and is sealed into a small diameter, protective stainless steel tube and anchored at the ends. A miniature electromagnet is fitted precisely at the centre of the wire inside the tube, and the tensioned wire plucked by energising the magnet. The resonant frequency is proportional to the square root of the tension in the wire. Strain is calculated by applying calibration factors and temperature compensation to the frequency measured.

Vibrating wire gauges are widely used and are available in a range of designs for different situations, eg embedded in concrete, welded to reinforcement, or grouted or epoxy bonded onto the surface of the concrete structure. They range in length up to 250 mm, can measure strains up to 3000 micro-strain, and are sensitive to about one micro-strain. They are suitable for automated monitoring of strain provided they are adequately protected from moisture ingress. Vibrating wire gauges are durable and widely used for geotechnical monitoring, but are not suitable for dynamic strain situations because of their slow response.

3.3.2.5 *Optical fibre strain gauge*

These strain gauges are increasingly used for monitoring strain and displacement in concrete structures because of the advantages they offer over conventional strain gauges, such as:

- the ability to measure strain at discrete points along the length of a single sensor (applicable to some sensors), which may be 100 m long
- low signal loss
- immunity from corrosion and electromagnetic interference
- durability
- ease of installation.

They are also more sensitive than other sensors, being able to measures strains as low as 0.1 micro-strain.

Optical fibre sensors measure strain by analysing the change in light characteristics transmitted through the fibre when strained. Any change in geometry of the fibre (eg due to bending, stretching or compression) affects the light signal transmitted. Bending a fibre results in some loss of transmitted light into the protective coating and stretching causes a shift in wavelength of the transmitted light. These changes in light properties form the basis of fibre optic sensing.

An optical fibre sensor consists of a thin glass fibre, typically 5 microns in diameter, with a thick plastic coating and jacket to protect it from physical damage and chemical attack by the alkaline concrete (glass is attacked by alkaline environments). The fibre itself is covered with a thin plastic cladding, typically 125 micron thick, the purpose of which is to ensure that light waves transmitted down the fibre are totally reflected internally and do not escape into the surrounding coating. To achieve this, the cladding has a slightly lower refractive index than the glass fibre. The bond between the glass fibre and the plastic coating is sufficiently strong to transmit strains in the enclosing concrete structure to the fibre itself. Fibre optic sensors have proved to be robust when embedded in concrete structures, despite the fragility of the glass fibre.

There are several types of fibre optic sensors, with the interferometric (eg SOFO, Fabry-Perot), Bragg grating, Brillouin and micro-bending sensors being most commonly used in civil engineering. The first type measures changes at the end of a single fibre. The spectrometric or Bragg grating sensors measure the change in wavelength at discrete, short sections of a single fibre containing gratings, Brillouin sensors measure frequency or refractive index change due to strain along the fibre length, while micro-bending sensors measure displacement at locations along the length of the fibre. Interferometric type sensors mostly measure strain at a single point on a fibre (some sensors can also be joined in series along a single fibre), while the other sensors measure strain along the fibre length, and are referred to as distributed sensors. Distributed sensors, especially those measuring strain along the full fibre length, have obvious advantages over point or localised sensors.

Interferometric type sensors include the low-coherence double Michelson (SOFO), and Fabry-Perot designs. Basically, they measure the interference of light from two identical fibres, one the sensor, the other a reference. The Michelson interferometer consists of two parallel fibres with mirrors at the ends, which are enclosed in a rigid tube embedded in the concrete. The sensing fibre measures displacement between the end plates of the sensor tube, while the other fibre is loosely held in the tube so that it is free from strain and serves as a reference and for measuring temperature. The system is based on measuring changes in the physical properties of the guided light, using an interferometer: the phase difference between light returned down the fibres is compared to determine strain. Up to 2000, the SOFO system had been used in more than 50 structures including bridges, tunnels, piles, anchored walls and nuclear power plants (Inaudi *et al*, 2000).

The Fabry-Perot sensor is available in several versions including extrinsic and intrinsic (reflective and transmissive). The extrinsic version consists of an optic fibre housed in a silica capillary tube with a small break or air gap of 10 to 100 microns in the fibre. Part of the light transmitted down the fibre is reflected at the air-fibre boundary in the gap. When the fibre is strained, the gap changes shape and causes the light frequency to change, which is related to the degree of strain.

Interferometric sensors measure strain at a single location, which may be over distances up to 20 metres and have a resolution of 2 micron. They cannot be connected together in the same optic fibre so separate fibres need to be embedded in the structure to measure strain at different locations.

The fibre Bragg grating sensor (FBG) has a periodic variation of the refractive index along a short section of an optical fibre, typically 10mm. This periodic variation or grating is formed by the interference of two ultraviolet lasers directed into the fibre from opposite sides. When a broadband light beam is transmitted down the fibre, a particular wavelength corresponding to the period of refractive index variation is preferentially reflected. Monitoring the shift in these peaks of light due to an imposed stress enables the strain at each grating to be measured – a spectrometer is used for measuring light wavelength. Fibre Bragg grating sensors have a maximum resolution of +/- 10 micro-strain, which is less than the +/- 0.01 micro-strain resolution of Fabry-Perot sensors. Bragg grating sensors have the advantage of reading absolute values, which means that they are unaffected by interrupted measurements. In the case of Fabry-Perot sensors, a new calibration has to be made every time a reading is interrupted (stopped).

The advantage of Bragg sensors is that many separate gratings can be installed on a single fibre, with each grating made to reflect at a different wavelength providing a strain reading. This is referred to as wavelength division multiplexing. In this way it is possible to multiplex more than 10 fibre-grating sensors along a single fibre, and by combining time-division multiplexing with wavelength dispersion multiplexing, many Bragg grating sensors can be installed on a single fibre.

The microbend sensor measures displacement and consists of an optic fibre twisted with other fibres or metallic wires (Lau, 2003). Elongation of the twisted fibres caused by movement of a structure will strain the optical fibre, which results in light escaping and a loss in transmitted light intensity. The intensity of the transmitted light is measured with an optical time domain reflectometer. Resolution is typically 30 microns for short periods, and 100 microns for longer periods, and is more appropriate for short-term, dynamic monitoring. A microbend sensor can measure displacements along the full length of a fibre and is a distributed sensor.

Brillouin scattering sensors show potential for distributed strain and temperature monitoring. They can measure strain or temperature variations in fibres with lengths up to 50 km with spatial resolution down to less than one meter.

In addition to strain, fibre optic sensors can also be used for measuring cracking in concrete structures. In the zigzag sensor, an optical fibre is embedded in concrete in a zigzag pattern and the attenuation of backscattered light measured as a function of time with an optical time domain reflectometer (Leung, 2001). Cracking in the enclosing concrete distorts the fibre, resulting in light loss by scattering and absorption in the fibre cladding. The sensor can locate cracking at any point on the fibre.

Fibre optic sensors can be joined in various configurations to form distributed or multiplexed sensing systems. In a multiplexed system, a single instrument transmits to and analyses light received from many separate sensors. In a distributed system, separate sensing points are located along a single optic fibre. Bragg grating and microbend sensors can form combined multiplexed and distributed systems, whereas other fibre optic sensors can form multiplexed systems.

Fibre optic sensors can be purchased separately, but are usually sold as complete systems because of the cost and expertise required to install and operate them. Inaudi *et al* (2000) provide general guidance on the installation of optic fibre systems.

3.3.2.6 *Strain gauges compared*

The strain gauges described in the previous sections each have advantages and limitations in particular situations as summarised in Table 3.3.

The most widely used strain gauges for automated monitoring of concrete structures are conventional electrical resistance and vibrating wire gauges. Electrical strain gauges in particular have limitations for long-term monitoring because of embrittlement and debonding of the resin, creep or fatigue of the sensor foil and measurement drift with time. This has encouraged their increasing replacement with optical fibre strain gauges. Vibrating wire gauges have advantages for long-term monitoring because they are free from drift, but are larger in size and more costly than inexpensive electrical strain gauges. Both electrical resistance and vibrating wire gauges have the disadvantage of only monitoring a limited area, which means that many gauges may need to be installed on a structure to adequately cover the areas susceptible to future damage.

The main focus in improved monitoring of strain in structures is the use of optical fibres because of their inherent advantages of long-term stability, ruggedness, freedom from corrosion, immunity to electromagnetic noise and lightning strikes, very low signal loss, and the potential to monitor large areas over the length of a single sensor. Their limitations, however, are high equipment cost and the expertise required to maintain the instrumentation and interpret the results.

Table 3.3 *Advantages and limitations of different types of strain gauge*

Sensor/gauge type	Advantages	Limitations
Mechanical	□ simple to use and interpret □ surface mounted, robust □ strain, crack or displacement monitoring □ gauge length 50 – 100 mm □ sensitivity typically 2 micro-strain	□ cannot be embedded in concrete □ usually used for manual monitoring □ not suitable for dynamic monitoring.
Electrical resistance	□ good sensitivity (1 micron) □ low cost and easy to install □ surface mounted or embedded □ easily automated.	□ limited to small strain lengths □ affected by electromagnetic noise □ surface preparation, temperature and humidity affect performance □ measurement drift □ limited fatigue life.
Vibrating wire (acoustic)	□ good sensitivity (1 micron) □ good long-term stability □ robust, easy to install □ direct frequency output suitable for digital measurement (no A-D converter required) □ can also be used for measuring displacements.	□ not for dynamic monitoring because of slow response □ affected by electromagnetic noise □ requires protection from moisture penetration □ sensor and instrumentation costly.
Fibre optic	□ very good sensitivity (0.1micron) □ can monitor strain, cracks, displacement □ can measure strain at multiple points with one fibre (Bragg grating sensor) or along the full length (Brillouin scattering and microbending sensors) □ good long-term stability □ combines sensor function and signal carrier (optical transmission) □ easily embedded or surface mounted □ not affected by electromagnetic noise □ not susceptible to corrosion and vibrations.	□ monitoring instrumentation costly □ cannot be repaired □ care needed in handling and embedding cable (usually placed next to rebar) □ experience needed to analyse results, maintain system □ sensitive to temperature change, which has to be monitored separately.

3.3.3 Crack and displacement

3.3.3.1 *General*

Crack and displacement gauges are installed to monitor the movement of new and existing structures. The most common applications are monitoring the change in width of an existing crack and the settlement of structures. Some of the methods described in Section 3.3.2 for strain measurement are applicable and most of the introduction to that section is relevant. All have an electrical output and can be automated for remote monitoring.

3.3.3.2 *Mechanical gauge*

The mechanical gauges used for measuring strain are also used for measuring displacement, ie movement between two points fixed to the structure is amplified by a spring lever system and is indicated by dial or digital means. Demec gauges are available for measuring displacements up to 100 mm with an accuracy of 0.01mm (Mayes Instruments Ltd, UK). The demec gauge is normally installed and removed after each measurement, but the digital version can be adapted for remote monitoring (see Section 3.3.2.2).

3.3.3.3 *Inductive displacement transducer*

Included here are the linear variable differential transducer (LVDT), differential variable reluctance transducer (DVRT), linear resistance transducer (LRT) and magnetostrictive transducer gauges. They measure displacement and, with the exception of the DVRT sensor, are not strain-based but they can measure very small changes in length so are also used as strain gauges.

An LVDT gauge is an electro-mechanical device that produces an AC voltage output in proportion to the relative displacement between the transformer and armature. They can be surface mounted or installed in purposely-drilled holes across existing cracks on structures, but are not suitable for embedding in concrete, so their main use is for monitoring crack or structural movement (eg Figure 3.3). They are suitable for both static and dynamic displacement monitoring. They are available for a wide range of displacements, from less than 1 mm to over 200 mm. Resolution and repeatability are excellent, and a resolution of less than 2 microns on a 2 mm stroke is achievable.

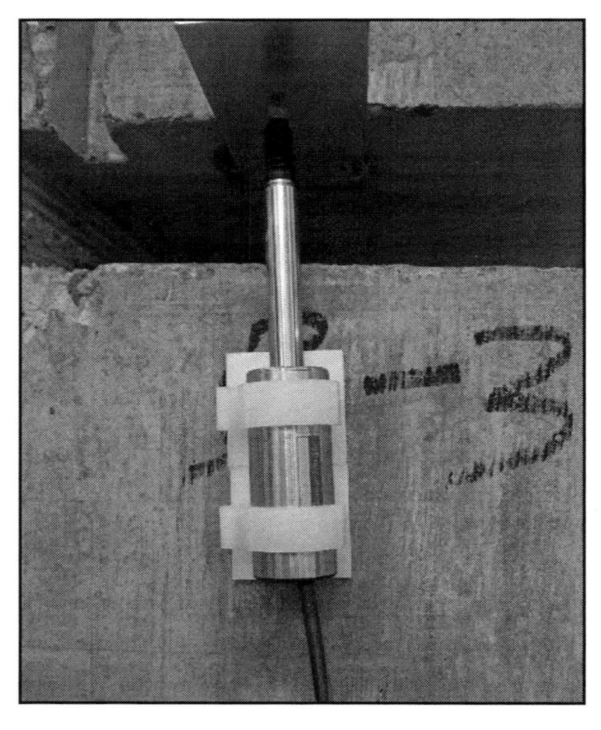

Figure 3.3

LVDT monitoring of a half joint

DVRT sensors operate on a similar principle to LVDT sensors, in which the moving armature position is detected by measuring the differential reluctance in the surrounding coil. This differential method provides a sensitive measure of rod position, while cancelling out temperature effects. The transducer mechanism is sealed in epoxy and housed within a stainless steel case. DVRT sensors are able to withstand demanding environments, and are now being developed for embedding in concrete.

3.3.3.4 *Electrical resistance crack propagation gauge*

A crack propagation gauge is designed to monitor the relative progress of a crack across the surface of (or inside) a structure. They can also be used to detect the onset of cracking. The gauge consists of a parallel arrangement of metal foil strands, connected to a common foil at their ends. When bonded to a surface, the progression of a surface crack through the gauge causes the strands to break, producing successive open circuits, which increase the total resistance of the sensor. A gauge consists typically of 10 – 20 cross-strands over a sensing depth of up to 10 mm, and they can be monitored remotely because they are resistance-based.

A simpler type of gauge, referred to as a crack detection gauge, is designed to indicate when a crack has reached a particular position. The resistor strands operate independently, each producing an open circuit when broken, which provides an early warning of crack movements to unacceptable limits.

3.3.3.5 *Electrolytic tilt sensor*

Electrolytic tilt sensors are used in various level sensing devices. They are resistance potentiometers, and consist of vertical electrodes held in a chamber filled with a conductive liquid. When the chamber is tilted, the liquid level remains horizontal causing the length of each electrode immersed in the conductive liquid to change, which alters their resistance. The resistance of the sensor changes in proportion to the angle of tilt. These sensors are rugged, passive devices that are cheap, have excellent repeatability, stability and accuracy (one second of an arc) when operating at low frequencies, and can be used in environments exposed to extreme temperature, humidity and shock. Temperature variations do affect the performance of the sensor, depending on the design. Tilt sensors are commonly used in gauges for monitoring ground excavations, boreholes (inclinometers) and the stability of structures (tiltmeters or beam sensors). The electrical output from the sensors allows them to be used for remote monitoring.

3.3.3.6 *Lasers*

Computer controlled laser theodolites may be used to automatically monitor the position of buildings and ground, typically during site excavations and construction, and raise an alarm when pre-set limits are exceeded. Laser-based surveying systems on the market can measure distances up to 200 m with a resolution of 1.5 mm. The development of a new type of laser strainmetre consisting of a laser beam projected inside a 650 m long pipe has been reported for measuring earthquake displacements (Southern California Earthquake Center, USA), with a resolution of less than 200 microns over this distance.

3.3.3.7 *Crack/displacement monitoring gauges based on various sensor types*

1. **Tiltmeters** measure the tilt in structures and are designed for surface mounting. They use a range of sensor types including electrolytic, servo accelerometer, and vibrating wire sensors.
2. **Inclinometers** measure the lateral displacement of soil and rock foundations, and of structures themselves, and are usually placed down boreholes. The inclinometer consists of a servo-accelerometer sensor housed in a steel tube with guide wheels. It is inserted down a borehole and readings taken at set intervals as it is raised. The inclinometer may be left permanently in place, with several linked together, and as such serves as a tiltmeter.
3. **Crackmeters** are intended for measuring movement across surface cracks or joints. They consist of a vibrating wire or other type of sensor that is placed on the surface across the crack or joint and held rigidly by pins on either side of the crack.
4. **Jointmeters** employ vibrating wire or inductive type transducer sensors, and are used for measuring movement between joint surfaces as well as mass movement in concrete structures.
5. **Extensometers** are designed for measuring dimensional changes over longer distances than crack or jointmeters and use vibrating wire and potentiometer sensors. There are different types for specific applications, eg tape extensometer for measuring movement between tunnel walls, and a borehole extensometer to measure deformations in concrete, foundations or soils.

6 **Rebar strain/strandmeters** consist of a vibrating wire or other type of sensor that is clamped at its ends to a steel rebar or cable for measuring strains and displacements.

3.3.3.8 *Crack/displacement gauges compared*

The advantages and limitations of various crack and displacement gauges are listed in Table 3.4.

Table 3.4 *Advantages and limitations of different types of displacement/crack gauge*

Sensor/ gauge type	Advantages	Limitations
Mechanical	□ simple to use and interpret □ surface mounted, robust □ gauge length 50 – 100 mm □ sensitivity typically 2 micro-strain.	□ cannot be embedded in concrete □ usually used for manual monitoring □ not suitable for dynamic monitoring.
LVDT gauge	□ low cost because of wide use □ environmentally robust □ high signal/noise, low output □ short response time □ good sensitivity (<2 microns) □ fast dynamic response.	□ dynamic measurements limited to less than 0.1 of LVDT resonant frequency □ cannot be embedded in concrete.
Electrical resistance crack propagation gauge	□ can measure the onset of cracking □ simple design □ easily automated □ can be embedded in concrete □ reliable.	□ resolution limited by spacing of wires (eg 0.25mm) □ need to protect from environment.
Vibrating wire (acoustic) gauge	□ good long-term stability □ robust, easy to install □ unaffected by long cable runs.	□ not for dynamic monitoring because of slow response □ affected by electromagnetic noise. □ requires protection from moisture penetration □ sensor and instrumentation costly.
Electrolytic tilt sensor (used in displacement gauges such as inclinometers, tiltmeters, beam sensors)	□ very accurate (one arc second) □ excellent repeatability, stability □ can be surface mounted or placed down borehole.	□ temperature corrections required □ fragile □ cannot be embedded in concrete.
Servo accelerometer (used in tiltmeters, inclinometers)	□ high accuracy, resolution (a few milli-gs) □ reliable □ good temperature stability.	□ not for dynamic monitoring □ more bulky than other accelerometers.

3.3.4 STRESS

Stress is defined as force per unit area, expressed in units of N/mm^2 or MPa. Stress is monitored in only a few situations in concrete structures because strain is a more functional measure of physical change and so is more easily measured (Section 3.3.2).

Stress is measured using strain gauges that are configured to measure force per unit area. Most of the strain gauges used are the vibrating wire type (Section 3.3.2.4), but include LVDT displacement (Section 3.3.3.3) and electrical resistance strain (Section 3.3.2.3) gauges. Types of stress gauge include stressmeters, load cells and total pressure cells.

Pressure cells consist of two thin metal plates welded together at the edges, with the gap between them filled with hydraulic oil. A vibrating wire transducer is connected to the cell by a short length of steel tubing, forming a closed hydraulic system. Both cell and transducer are embedded in the medium to be monitored, which could be soil, concrete or the interface between the two. Typical applications include monitoring radial or tangential stress in tunnel linings (up to 20 MPa), total pressure and stress distribution within embankments and dams (up to 20 MPa), contact pressure on diaphragm and retaining walls, piers and abutments, foundation bearing pressures, and pressures on and within linings of underground excavations.

An interesting application was the installation of 60 pressure cells at the bottom of the 452 m high Petronas Towers in Kuala Lumpur. Their purpose was to monitor the behaviour of the 4.5 m thick concrete rafts on which each tower was built. Due to the soft ground conditions, a layer of concrete was placed to act as a working platform, with boxed out sections for installing the pressure cells. The earth at the bottom of these openings was carefully levelled and cells were placed sensitive-face down, flush with the bottom of the platform. Readings are taken twice a year.

3.3.5 Acoustic emission

The acoustic emission method measures high-frequency acoustic energy emitted from a structure undergoing stress due to physical or thermal loading. Acoustic emissions are sound or ultrasound pulses generated when a solid structure is stressed to a sufficiently high level. The acoustic emissions are derived from local disturbances in the structure such as micro-cracking, dislocation movement, and inter-granular friction. The method is used to monitor bridge tendons, and has been proposed as a method to measure reinforcement corrosion (Section 3.4.8).

The energy released during stressing is very small and requires the use of sensitive sensors and signal processing electronics or software to distinguish event signals from extraneous background noise. Piezoelectric sensors are placed at selected points on a structure and connected to instrumentation at a central monitoring station where the acoustic signals are analysed by computer to distinguish real from false events. The location of the acoustic emission signals can be determined by calculating the difference in time taken for a pulse to arrive at the different transducers. Acoustic emission provides a means of monitoring a structure continuously.

Acoustic monitoring is similar to acoustic emission monitoring, but differs in that it records the sound of actual failures of components. To date the most successful applications have been monitoring wire breaks in bridge support cables (eg Figure 3.4) and in prestressed concrete pipelines, including the Great Man-Made River pipeline in Libya.

Figure 3.4

Acoustic sensor (courtesy Advitam)

Acoustic (emission) monitoring has found limited use for monitoring concrete itself. The main reason is the high degree of attenuation suffered by acoustic waves in concrete, especially reinforced concrete. Noise events do not generate enough energy to propagate far across the structure surface. Research continues, however, into ways to apply the method more successfully to concrete structures, such as detecting reinforcement corrosion (Section 3.4.8), mainly because of the potential the method has to monitor large structures non-intrusively.

3.3.6 Acceleration/vibration

Concrete structures are often subject to vibration effects from moving road or rail traffic, or sudden movements due to earthquakes, which may cause rapid or progressive long-term damage. Accelerometers are widely used for monitoring the effects of vibration in structures.

An accelerometer measures how fast the speed of an object is changing, and produces an electrical signal proportional to the magnitude, frequency and amplitude of the shock or vibration experienced. There are several types of accelerometer including piezoelectric, servo (force-balance), piezo-resistive and capacitive, but the basic principle of operation is the same in most types. A known mass is held and usually centred by springs inside a rigid housing that is fixed to the structure. When subjected to shock, the mass does not accelerate as fast as the housing because of its inertia and is displaced relative to the housing. The amount of this displacement is measured with a sensor.

Servo accelerometers use a pendulous, high-magnetic permeability mass hung from a hinge. The null position at rest is maintained by a counterbalancing force applied through a magnetic coil. When subjected to acceleration, the mass is displaced with the coil current needed to maintain the null position proportional to the accelerating force. Servo accelerometers have the best temperature stability, are more sensitive than other accelerometers and are usually used for static monitoring situations. They are larger in size than other types of accelerometers, and cannot withstand high shock situations.

Piezoelectric accelerometers are generally the most rugged type and are usually housed in a metal case that is robust enough for embedding in concrete (eg Figure 3.5). They consist of a crystal sensor that emits an electric charge when subjected to an accelerating force and many types have internal electronic circuitry to convert the high impedance output into a low impedance signal, which allows direct electrical output to data logging and control systems. They are most suitable for low frequencies and acceleration.

Figure 3.5 *Piezo-electric accelerometer*

Recent technology developments have allowed accelerometers to be miniaturised, and their functionality to be improved with on-board memory. An increasing number of micro-sized accelerometers using semiconductor technology are now becoming available.

Selection of an accelerometer requires consideration of many factors, the most important being frequency response and acceleration capability. The most common applications of accelerometers in civil engineering are the measurement of bridge vibrations due to traffic or use in tiltmeters and inclinometers for measuring movement in structures such as dam walls. The level of vibration in these situations is generally low, so accelerometers with high sensitivity and the ability to operate with low g forces are required. For static situations, servo type accelerometers are usually the best choice. Other factors include nature of shock (direction, uniaxial or triaxial forces, shear, compressive or bending forces, etc), ambient temperature range, and type of environment (chemical, electromagnetic). The many types and wide performance range of accelerometers on the market make selection difficult so manufacturers and suppliers are best placed to provide advice on a particular application.

3.3.7 Methods under development

Electro-optic methodologies, especially those based on lasers, promise improved approaches to inspection. One of the most-studied techniques is *digital shearography*. This directly measures the strain deformation of surfaces by capturing the deformation gradient rather than the deformation itself. Digital shearography requires only three basic elements:

1. An illumination system.
2. An interferometer.
3. Software to drive the acquisition of the images.

An expander breaks a laser into a collection of beams aimed at the material. Reflected beams pass through an interferometer, and a CCD camera records the results, or speckle patterns. The method has now been developed to provide a full-field video picture of the strain pattern, in real time, over large areas of a structure. Shearography has been successfully applied in the aerospace and car industries, and is being investigated for the detection of cracks, voids and corrosion in civil engineering structures. The instrumentation is reportedly robust and easily manoeuvred. As presently designed and operated, measurements are carried out by moving the equipment manually. The methods, however, appear suitable for remote monitoring using permanently mounted equipment covering the critical parts of the structure, eg concrete nuclear reactor shells.

A major factor contributing to the deterioration of concrete road bridges is traffic overload caused by heavy trucks. The USA Department of Transportation has investigated the use of *transformation-induced plasticity (TRIP) steel sensors* for monitoring peak load/strain history (Chase and Washer, 1997). TRIP is a special steel that undergoes a permanent change in crystal structure from non-magnetic to magnetic, in proportion to the peak strain. A TRIP sensor has been tested on the Fred Hartman bridge over the Houston ship canal (Chase and Washer, 1997).

Ultrasonic methods include a range of techniques using transducers and surface impact to apply a stress wave to the structure and record the returned signal. They are sometimes used in the routine, on-site inspection of concrete structures to determine relative condition, cracking, delamination, voids, honeycombing, member thickness, and for more specific problems such as the condition of piles. The transducers and impact instrumentation used, however, are designed for manual use and are not suited to permanent installation throughout a structure. No reports have been found of permanent monitoring systems based on ultrasonic methods. Coupling transducers to the structure is critical and usually achieved using a grease or adhesive. The development of non-contact transducers may extend the usefulness of ultrasonics to remote monitoring.

Conductive paint has been proposed as a method for detecting cracks in concrete tunnel linings (Okada *et al*, 2001). A highly conductive paint containing carbon is painted in lines 2 – 3 cm wide along the tunnel wall, and the conductance monitored. Cracks that develop in the concrete cause a break in the paint and affect its conductance. Conductive paint is used for anodes in cathodic protection systems, and is available commercially. Conductive paint provides an electrical output, so it is adaptable to remote monitoring. The method, however, only appears suitable for use in protected environments where the paint is not damaged by weather or service conditions. Water contaminated with salts may bridge cracks or otherwise affect the conductivity of the paint and result in spurious indications, but this may be overcome by waterproofing with another paint.

3.4 REINFORCING STEEL CORROSION

3.4.1 Introduction

The corrosion of reinforcing steel and consequent cracking of the surrounding concrete is the most serious and costly form of damage to concrete structures. This section concerns the monitoring of corrosion. The main methods described are:

- half-cell potential (Section 3.4.2)
- resistivity (Section 3.4.3)

- galvanic current (Section 3.4.4)
- linear polarisation resistance (Section 3.4.5)
- electrical resistance (loss of cross-section) (Section 3.4.6)
- electrochemical noise (Section 3.4.7).

Methods under development are described in Section 3.4.8. Brief reference is made to data logging instrumentation required for storing and transmitting the signal by cable or telemetry to a remote computer. Data loggers are standard instrumentation that can accept and transmit an electrical signal, and may also perform control functions such as switching a sensor on or off at pre-set intervals to take a reading or to conserve battery power. More detailed information on data logging and transmission systems is provided in Section 3.9.

Concrete normally protects reinforcing steel. During cement hydration the liquid phase rapidly acquires a high pH that is buffered to resist downward changes in pH by the hydration products of cement. When steel is in contact with such an alkaline solution a passive oxide film covers the surface, presenting a barrier to further metal loss. Conditions may arise, however, that render the passive film unstable, leading to corrosion of the reinforcing steel. The two most important causes of this are carbonation and chloride contamination of the concrete.

Carbonation is a phenomenon that occurs in all atmospherically exposed concrete, but is usually only a significant problem for buildings. A reduction in the pH of the concrete pore solution, which renders the passive film unstable, is induced by the dissolution of atmospheric carbon dioxide in the pore solution. The carbonation process and factors influencing it are described in Section 4.3.4. Chloride contamination may originate from an internal source (ie from the mix ingredients) or from an external source. Internal sources include contamination of the aggregate (for example due to inadequate washing of marine dredged material) and the use of calcium chloride as a set accelerator. Limitations are placed by current codes of practice on the acceptable levels of chloride contamination resulting from the use of contaminated mix materials, while the use of chloride-containing admixtures for concrete is generally not permitted. Internal chlorides tend to affect only older existing structures. External sources of chlorides include de-icing salts and seawater. Mechanisms by which chlorides penetrate concrete and influencing factors are discussed in Section 4.3.3.

Once passive film breakdown has occurred, a corrosion cell is established. No physical damage occurs before this stage. A current flows between the anodic areas, where metal dissolution occurs, and the cathodic areas, where oxygen is reduced. Corrosion rates may be expressed as a current density, a rate of weight loss, or a rate of section loss. For steel, a corrosion current of 1 mA/m^2 approximates a weight loss of 10 g/m^2yr, which in turn approximates to a section loss of 1 $\mu m/yr$. Reinforcing steel corrosion rates of less than 1 mA/m^2 are considered to be negligible and are unlikely to result in damage to the concrete. Higher corrosion rates are considered to be significant and, if oxygen has relatively easy access to the steel (the pore system is not saturated with water), the general corrosion rate may exceed 100 mA/m^2. Local corrosion rates of 1000 mA/m^2 are possible. The products of corrosion are usually of far greater volume than the steel consumed and so corrosion results not only in loss of the cross-sectional area of rebars, but also cracking and spalling of the concrete. The exception to this is anaerobic corrosion, which is known to occur only very rarely, where corrosion takes place under oxygen starved conditions and the resulting black corrosion product is of low volume.

Most proven corrosion monitoring methods are based on measuring electrochemical changes in the steel, or the consequences of such changes, because steel corrosion is an electrochemical process involving the movement of ions under the influence of an electrical potential. The purpose of electrochemical methods is to assess the corrosion state of reinforcing steel in concrete, either directly by measuring the corrosion rate of the steel using linear polarisation (Section 3.4.5) or electrical resistance (Section 3.4.6) methods, or indirectly by providing an indication of the risk of corrosion using potential (Section 3.4.2), resistivity (Section 3.4.3), galvanic (Section 3.4.4) or concrete chemistry (Section 3.7) methods.

Electrochemical methods are suitable for remote monitoring in concrete structures because they provide an electrical output signal that can be transmitted over long distances by cable or wireless means.

Case studies describing the application of corrosion monitoring sensors to actual structures are provided in Appendix 2 of DTI Report 1.

3.4.2 Half-cell potential

The corrosion of reinforcing steel involves the reduction of iron by oxygen to form rust at active corroding, anodic sites. This reduction releases electrons, which flow to the cathodic areas on the reinforcement, producing a negative charge. The half-cell potential method is used to measure this charge and so provide an indication of corrosion condition.

Half-cell potential monitoring is widely used for manual on-site assessment of reinforcing steel corrosion because the method is easy to understand, the equipment simple to use and it provides some guidance on the probability of reinforcing steel corrosion. A (half-cell) reference electrode is placed on the concrete surface and connected to adjacent embedded steel reinforcement through a high impedance voltmeter. The reference electrode is usually the copper/copper sulphate type (a copper rod immersed in a solution of copper sulphate) with the contact end covered with a wetted porous plug to provide good electrical continuity with the concrete pore solution. Potential measurements are taken on a grid pattern on the concrete surface and are plotted to provide a potential contour map of the surface. ASTM C 876 provides guidance (ASTM, 1999).

For automated monitoring of existing structures, reference electrodes are retrofitted into a hole drilled in the concrete and sealed with mortar. For new structures, electrodes are embedded in the cover concrete or within the reinforcing steel cage region during casting. Permanently installed electrolytic electrodes (ie solid metallic bar in an electrolyte, which may be a solution or a gel) suffer the problem of leakage of electrolyte, which limits their life and stability. When they are used in soil they are regularly removed for servicing and replacement of expended electrolyte. Clearly it is not possible to calibrate them or check their calibration when they are embedded in mortar or concrete. This is not a problem when using reference electrodes for monitoring cathodic protection systems or when making linear polarisation measurements (Section 3.4.5) because in these cases it is the short-term shift in potential that is of interest. However, for long-term monitoring this is a major drawback. The most common electrolytic reference electrodes of this type used for embedding in concrete are the silver/silver chloride and manganese/manganese dioxide electrodes.

Thousands of reference electrodes have been installed in cathodic protection systems in the UK and Europe over the past 20 years. Once successfully installed, they have generally remained serviceable. Failure of reference electrodes in bridge decks has commonly been reported in the US, but this may be a consequence of poor installation and/or the influence of traffic. Limited data is available regarding the long-term stability of reference electrodes in situations where absolute (not relative) potential readings are required.

Concerns regarding the effects of long-term leakage of electrolyte from embedded electrolytic electrodes have encouraged interest in pseudo-electrodes that show a very long life. Pseudo-electrodes consist of bare metals, such as graphite, stainless steel, lead and zinc or the mixed metal oxide/titanium electrode embedded directly in concrete. They are, however, less stable than the conventional electrolytic reference electrodes, as the interface that produces the electrochemical reaction against which the steel/concrete interface potential is measured is exposed to changes in the environment itself, and so will be affected by changes in moisture and pore solution chemistry more directly than an electrolytic electrode.

A system for on-line monitoring of half-cell potentials is simple to design and install, consisting of a half-cell and instrumentation to measure the voltage and relay the signal to a remote computer. Measurement is typically via a high impedance (minimum 20 Mohm) analogue to digital converter reading voltage to one millivolt.

Experience from field and laboratory testing has provided data for estimating the probability of corrosion as a function of the measured potential. Potentials more negative than -350 mV (based on copper/copper sulphate electrode) are usually associated with a high risk of corrosion. However many factors affect the potential measured in concrete in addition to the corrosion state of the reinforcing steel, including oxygen, chloride, pH and moisture levels and concrete resistivity. So it is usual to assess reinforcement corrosion risk in terms of relative susceptibility rather than absolute potential values.

Half-cell electrodes are commonly embedded in concrete to monitor the potential of structures for possible rebar corrosion, for stray currents from nearby railway systems and to assess the effectiveness of repairs or inhibitor systems. Potential monitoring is usually combined with resistivity monitoring for a more definitive conclusion because potential depends on resistivity. Potential is also measured as part of the linear polarisation (Section 3.4.5) and electrochemical noise (Section 3.4.7) methods.

3.4.3 Concrete resistivity

The corrosion of steel reinforcement in concrete generates an electric current that flows through the concrete, the charge carried by ions in the concrete pore solution. The lower the electrical resistivity of the concrete, the more readily current will flow and the greater the amount of reinforcement corrosion. So while half-cell potential monitoring (Section 3.4.2) establishes areas of possible corrosion activity, resistivity monitoring provides a semi-quantitative indication of the likely corrosion rate once corrosion has been initiated.

The resistivity of concrete is obtained by measuring the voltage drop when a current is passed between electrodes embedded within the concrete. An alternating current of typically 250 mA at a frequency of between 25 and 150 Hz is used, with a high resolution voltmeter (0.1 mV) for measuring the potential. Ohm's law is used to calculate the electrical resistance between the electrodes, which is multiplied by a cell constant (dependent on the shape, size and spacing of the electrodes) to determine the resistivity.

The electrodes are usually made of steel, but other metals and graphite are also used. There are many possible shapes and arrangements of electrodes, usually involving two or more parallel plates or pins. One factor to consider when selecting an appropriate electrode arrangement is whether it is desirable to monitor the variation in resistivity with depth into the concrete or simply the resistivity at one particular depth, usually the depth of the reinforcing steel. One popular design for embedding in new structures comprises a set of pairs of stainless pins, mounted on a small Perspex former and connected to the reinforcement. Each electrode is sleeved to expose 5 mm of the tip, and measurements are taken between electrode pairs. An equivalent design for retrofitting into a hole drilled into an existing structure consists of a stack of stainless steel rings sleeved onto a PVC rod and separated by rubber insulators with measurements taken between pairs of rings. An alternative method uses a single electrode on the surface and a connection to the reinforcement. In this way the resistivity of the full thickness of concrete cover is measured, however, concrete carbonation and concrete drying both dramatically increase resistivity and so, in some environments, surface effects may mask behaviour nearer the reinforcing steel.

If the electrode spacing is small in relation to the size of the coarse aggregate, measurements may be unduly dependent upon the local arrangement of aggregate particles. If the spacing is too large or the electrodes are too close to the reinforcement, the reinforcement may short circuit the current flow causing an underestimation of resistivity.

Electrical resistivity is a function of concrete mix ingredients and proportions, increasing with pulverized fuel ash (PFA) and slag (GGBS) content and reducing with a reduction in water/binder ratio. Resistivity reduces with increases in temperature and moisture content. Consequently, all else being equal, resistivity varies from day to night and with the seasons. Due to the many variables affecting resistivity measurements, an assessment of corrosion is based on a probability rating according to bands of resistivity values established from field and laboratory experience.

Instruments are available that can measure both resistivity and half-cell potential (eg Germann Instruments, Denmark and Proceq, Switzerland). Both resistivity and potential are measured when making corrosion rate measurements using the linear polarisation resistance method (Section 3.4.5).

3.4.4 Galvanic current

Galvanic current monitoring (also referred to as macro-cell monitoring, or zero resistance ammetry) uses steel anodes placed at different depths in the concrete cover to detect the rate at which chemical changes able to initiate corrosion penetrate the concrete.

The method is based on the principle that if two metals of differing electro-negativity are electrically coupled and exposed to an aggressive environment, the more negative metal (anode) will corrode in preference to the more noble electrode (cathode), at a rate that depends on the difference in electro-negativity between the two electrodes. When the anode corrodes freely, a small current is generated and can be measured by a zero resistance ammeter (used for measuring very low currents) or a voltmeter through a known resistance load. The potential of the corroding anode will decrease, and this is sometimes measured against a reference electrode to provide more information on the corrosion process.

Galvanic sensors are designed for embedding in concrete, and consist of several bars of steel (usually of the same composition as the reinforcing steel and often arranged as a ladder) as anodes separately connected to a cathode, eg platinum-coated steel. The sensor is normally placed in the cover concrete and orientated at an angle to the concrete surface so that the anodes are positioned at varying depths below the surface (see Figure 4.1).

Most galvanic sensors tend to be fairly large, varying in size from 10 cm to over 30 cm in length, and may compromise the integrity of the concrete cover. Care should be taken to ensure that concrete is properly compacted around the anodes. The first anodes to corrode (closest to surface) may cause cracking of the concrete, accelerating the corrosion of lower anodes giving a false picture of corrosion penetration. However, if they were smaller they would monitor a smaller, less representative, area.

Galvanic sensors are frequently marketed as chloride penetration sensors because chlorides cause more rapid corrosion of reinforcing steel than other variables in the environment, but they measure corrosion caused by any form of chemical attack of the steel. Galvanic sensors measure a simple change and the output current or potential is not subject to ambiguity of interpretation. The electrical output is suitable for automated monitoring.

Raupach and Schiessl (2001) reported that over 800 galvanic sensors were installed worldwide during the 1990s in tunnels, bridges, foundations and other structures exposed to aggressive environments.

3.4.5 Linear polarisation resistance

The linear polarisation resistance (LPR) method provides a direct, real time measurement of steel corrosion rate, and is the most commonly used method for measuring rebar corrosion, both remotely in the field and the laboratory. The term polarisation refers to the deviation from an equilibrium position, for example when a voltage is applied to an electrode.

The theory of LPR is well established and the method is widely used for measuring the corrosion of metals in a range of industrial processes. It is based on the linear relationship that occurs between the applied current density and potential within 10 mV of the rest potential of a freely corroding electrode. The relationship applies to a uniformly corroding electrode. An LPR system consists of a reference electrode (typically silver/silver chloride or manganese/manganese dioxide), a working electrode (the reinforcing steel), and a counter (or auxiliary) electrode through which a potential is applied to the reinforcement. The counter electrode is usually stainless steel or activated titanium. The reference and counter electrodes are embedded directly in the concrete with the electrical circuit being completed via the pore solution to the reinforcement. Measurements are taken by varying the current to maintain the working electrode at a constant potential (potentiostatic mode), or by varying the potential to maintain a constant current from the counter to the working electrode (galvanostatic mode).

The area of the working electrode (steel reinforcement) is required to determine the current density and as a result the corrosion rate because it affects the current flowing from the counter electrode to the working electrode. Uncertainty regarding the effective area of the embedded reinforcement involved leads to inaccuracy, but can be overcome in two ways:

1 Using a reinforcing bar of known area that has been purposely embedded in the concrete.

2 Using a secondary guard or auxiliary electrode surrounding the counter electrode to confine the applied current to a known area of the reinforcement.

The guard electrode is maintained at the same potential as the counter electrode, which has the effect of confining the current flowing from the working electrode to the region immediately below the counter electrode. However most guard electrode designs are not suitable for embedding in concrete, although some can be partially embedded.

LPR measures uniform corrosion, not pitting corrosion. This should be considered when interpreting LPR results, and limits the accuracy and application of the method when applied to chloride-induced corrosion.

Because LPR electrodes for remote monitoring are usually embedded in concrete, they cannot be inspected or their accuracy checked. A reliable reference electrode is essential for measuring the corrosion rate, and is usually a silver/silver chloride or manganese/ manganese dioxide electrode although pseudo reference electrodes that are stable over the period of measurement and do not degrade with time are also used (see Section 3.4.2).

A related method for measuring potential and corrosion rate is the *galvanostatic pulse* method. In this method, an anodic current pulse is impressed on the reinforcing steel for a short time using a counter current electrode positioned on the surface and the resultant potential change recorded relative to a reference electrode. The slope of the potential versus time curve is related to corrosion: passive reinforcement produces a high slope, whereas reinforcement undergoing corrosion shows a very small slope. The method is reportedly very rapid and may produce less ambiguous results compared to potential mapping, especially in wet or carbonated concrete.

LPR systems can be installed during construction or retrofitted into existing concrete structures. The design of new sensors is directed mainly at taking advantage of advances in electronics and miniaturisation, and improving their robustness and durability for embedding in the demanding concrete environment, especially road decks. For example, Virginia Technologies (USA) has developed an embeddable sensor that measures several parameters, including linear polarisation, open-circuit potential, resistivity and temperature. It also contains a silver/silver chloride electrode for estimating chloride concentration (see Section 3.7.2). The ECI-1 sensor unit contains a micro-controller to sequence the sensor measurements and to carry out the necessary calculations. Data is stored digitally on board in a local non-volatile memory, or can be transmitted directly via a network connection. The datalogger is powered by a battery backed up by a solar collector or by local electrical power lines, and is positioned externally to the structure and interfaces with a wireless transceiver or cell phone modem to provide remote data collection and operation.

3.4.6 Electrical resistance

The electrical resistance (ER) method is based on the increase in electrical resistance of a metal probe as it loses metal due to corrosion. Commercial ER sensors usually measure the resistance of the corroding probe relative to that of an identical, shielded (reference) probe. The temperature of the environment is monitored at the same time as it has a strong influence on the electrical resistivity of a metal. The resistive voltages developed across the probe elements are small, typically 10 to 100 μV, and difficult to measure with great accuracy. Higher sensitivities can be achieved by using thinner, higher resistance, elements, but this significantly reduces the life of the sensor.

The method is widely used for monitoring metallic corrosion in the process industries and has been adapted for measuring reinforcing steel corrosion although to date, there are few reports of its practical use for monitoring concrete structures. The Corrosometer from Rohrback Cosasco (USA) consists of a single, external probe made from the same steel as used for reinforcement. The probe is typically embedded parallel to the reinforcement within the concrete cover, to provide warning of impending reinforcement corrosion (similar to galvanic monitoring systems). It is not electrically connected to the reinforcing steel as is the case with linear polarisation sensors. Readout is in direct corrosion rate units, eg mm/yr.

A more recent development is the inductive resistance probe (Microcor from Rohrback Cosasco, USA), which operates on the same principle as the electrical resistance probe, but offers an instantaneous corrosion rate, comparable to the LPR method. Mass changes in the sensor element are detected by measuring changes in the inductive resistance of a coil located inside the element. For a given sensor element life, the probe will tend to show a change in corrosion rate much more quickly than the equivalent electrical resistance probe. The method is reported to be at least two orders of magnitude more sensitive than the corresponding electrical resistance probe, and like the latter can be used for low conductivity situations, where electrochemical methods are generally unstable.

A drawback of the electrical resistance method (as with the LPR method) is that it cannot reliably detect pitting corrosion because pits penetrate the probe and cause it to fail, but cause negligible material loss.

3.4.7 Electrochemical noise

Electrochemical noise refers to the random fluctuations in potential or current occurring during an electrochemical reaction such as steel corrosion. Noise measurements provide an instantaneous corrosion rate and an indication of the type of corrosion damage that is occurring, and can distinguish between general and localised attack, and different forms of localised corrosion such as pitting and stress corrosion cracking. The severity of localised corrosion can also be judged from the number and shape of the noise fluctuations. In theory, the combination of potential and current noise measurements can be used to estimate the corrosion rate, using methodology related to the linear polarisation resistance method (Section 3.4.5). Attractions of the technique are that there is no artificial disturbance of the system, unlike LPR where a potential shift is applied and it performs well under conditions of limited conductivity (typical of concrete).

Instrumentation required to perform electrochemical noise measurements includes a multi-meter, computer and spectrum analyser. Most electrochemical noise generation occurs at low-frequencies (one Hz or less). Probes for taking measurements are similar to those used in the LPR method. Some commercial instrumentation combines electrochemical noise with linear polarisation because both methods use the same electrode system. Electrochemical noise can be measured either as potential noise, for example the fluctuations of the free-corrosion potential of a corroding electrode, or as current noise, such as the fluctuations of the current required to polarise an electrode.

While the measurement of electrochemical noise is straightforward, analysis of the data to obtain meaningful results is complex. The usual approach is to transform time data into the frequency domain to give frequency spectra using fast Fourier transforms. Interpretation in the case of reinforcing steel is more complex than for chemical process industry applications. This is the main reason why, despite much research, there are few examples of electrochemical noise monitoring of concrete structures.

3.4.8 Methods under development

Electrical time domain reflectometry (ETDR) has been used for many years to detect faults in transmission lines. The method involves passing an electrical pulse along a transmission line system (ie two parallel wires) and using an oscilloscope to observe the echoes. Any discontinuity will cause a reflection. From the transit time, magnitude and polarity of the reflection, it is possible to determine the spatial location and nature of the discontinuity. The method has been applied to prestressed concrete bridge monitoring by installing a sensor wire near to the prestressing cable (Liu *et al*, 2002). Further development work, however, is needed to define more closely the limitations of the method, and to improve its sensitivity.

Fibre optic sensors are being investigated for the detection and measurement of corrosion in reinforced concrete either directly by measuring colour change due to rusting or indirectly by detecting cracking caused by expansion of the reinforcement corrosion product. Fibre optic sensor technology is well developed, with several different methods of measurement (Section 3.3.2.5).

Acoustic emission monitoring of concrete (Section 3.3.5) has been used in the laboratory to detect reinforcing steel corrosion and has been shown to detect film cracking, gas evolution, and microcracking. Although attenuation of the acoustic emission signal in the concrete is a concern, placement of the acoustic emission transducers on the reinforcing steel and use of the steel as the sound propagation medium allow the onset of steel corrosion to be detected. It should be possible to use the acoustic emission signal from different transducers to calculate the location where the steel corrosion is occurring.

3.4.9 Corrosion monitoring methods compared

All of the methods described in Sections 3.4.2 to 3.4.7 are suitable for automated monitoring as they provide an electrical output or a resistance change. The main advantages and limitations of these methods are listed in Table 3.5.

Table 3.5 *Advantages and limitations of methods for monitoring rebar corrosion*

Method	Advantages	Limitations
Half-cell potential	□ indicates risk of rebar corrosion □ equipment inexpensive and easy to use □ principle of method easy to understand.	□ semi-quantitative indication of risk of corrosion □ no indication of corrosion rate □ requires connection to embedded reinforcement □ concrete should be covered by closely spaced measurements for best result.
Resistivity	□ indicates rate of corrosion once corrosion initiated □ equipment inexpensive and easy to use □ principle of method easy to understand.	□ semi-quantitative indication of corrosion rate (if corrosion is initiated) □ concrete should be covered by closely spaced measurements for best result.
Galvanic current	□ measures rate of ingress of chemical or corrosive changes into concrete □ allows remedial action to be taken before rebar corrosion occurs □ not reliant on reference electrodes □ interpretation simple, unambiguous □ no power required.	□ large size of sensor may cause cracking of cover concrete when corrosion starts.
Linear polarisation resistance (LPR)	□ direct measurement of rebar corrosion rate □ can be fully embedded in concrete □ most common method for measuring rebar corrosion rate □ method measures potential shift so embedded reference electrode does not need calibration.	□ indicates uniform corrosion, not pitting □ measures reinforcement corrosion over limited area □ time required for current value to stabilise at a certain potential may take minutes to days depending on concrete resistivity. □ area of working electrode required in calculations.
Electrical resistance	□ measures corrosion rate of embedded steel probe □ can be fully or partly embedded in concrete.	□ indicates uniform corrosion, not pitting □ accumulation of corrosion product on probe may give misleading result □ sensor probe has limited life.
Electrochemical noise	□ indicates corrosion activity instantaneously □ measures pitting corrosion.	□ interpretation of results requires experience □ complex and costly instrumentation required.

3.5 CONCRETE TEMPERATURE

3.5.1 Introduction

It is common practice to embed sensors to monitor the temperature of concrete during the first few days of its life to determine its maturity, strength, and vulnerability to early age thermal cracking and determine when formwork should be removed. The temperature sensors may be left in place to provide long-term monitoring data relevant to structural integrity. Concrete structures expand and contract in response to diurnal variations in temperature, which can result in structural strain and cracking. The strain through a winter/summer cycle can be up to ten times greater than that due to service loading.

Most strain, corrosion and moisture sensors are affected by temperature and require temperature correction so temperature is the most commonly monitored parameter. Many strain, corrosion and humidity sensors have built-in temperature measurement. An examination of the case studies in Appendix A2.2 of DTI Report 1 illustrates the widespread use of temperature sensors, which may have been used in all of the case studies even when not referred to.

Temperature measurement in the exposure environment, such as air and soil, is covered in Section 3.8. Sensors for monitoring temperature in concrete include thermocouples, resistance thermometers, thermistors and fibre optics. They can be embedded in concrete at the time of casting or in drilled holes. Most require effective isolation from moisture and stray currents as their design involves wiring connections to the sensor except in the case of fibre optics, which are immune to electromagnetic effects. Most temperature sensors are accurate to less than ±1°C, which is more than adequate for general temperature monitoring and accurate enough for use in correcting readings obtained from other temperature-sensitive types of sensor.

3.5.2 Thermocouples

Thermocouples are the most common type of temperature sensing device used because they are robust, simple in operation and can measure temperature in virtually any situation, with different types covering the temperature range from -250°C to +2600°C.

Thermocouples use the Seebeck effect in which a temperature gradient along a conductor creates a voltage. A thermocouple consists of two wires, each made of a different homogeneous metal or alloy, insulated from each other along their length, and covered with an outer protection sheath. The wires are joined at one end to form a sensing or measuring junction, with the other end of the wires usually terminated at a measuring instrument where they form a reference junction. The reference junction is usually held at ambient temperature in practical situations. When the two junctions are at different temperatures the measured voltage between the junctions indicates the temperature difference.

Thermocouples are defined according to their alloy combinations that control their temperature ranges. The most common thermocouple used is Type K (NiCr and NiAl legs), with a temperature range of 0 to 1000°C for continuous use (-180 to +1300°C for short-term use), and a resolution of ±1.5°C (from -40 to +375°C). Type T thermocouples can measure to lower temperatures (-185 to +300°C), while those containing platinum such as Type B are used for high temperature applications up to 1700°C.

Practical limitations in the use of thermocouples are the need to maintain the reference junction at a fixed temperature to calculate the temperature at the measuring junction from the thermocouple output voltage, and the high cost of long cable runs.

3.5.3 Resistance thermometers

Resistance temperature devices, usually abbreviated to RTD, are slowly replacing thermocouples in many lower temperature industrial applications (below 600°C). Resistance thermometers are available in various construction forms and offer greater stability, accuracy and repeatability, and their resistance tends to be almost linear with temperature. Resistance thermometers generally measure temperature in the range -70 to +500°C, to a resolution of ±0.3°C. They are very linear and accurate, however, they are typically more expensive than other temperature measuring methods.

Resistance thermometers determine temperature by measuring the change in resistance of an electrical conductor to current flow and so need a small power source. Platinum in wire or film is usually used as the conductor due to its stability with temperature. The sensor element is available in many forms, the most common being wire wound in a ceramic insulator (for high temperatures to 850°C), wires encapsulated in glass (resists the highest vibration and offers most protection to the platinum), and thin film with a platinum film on a ceramic substrate (mass produced so inexpensive). Special extension cables or cold junction compensations are not required as for thermocouples so inexpensive copper cabling can be used.

3.5.4 Thermistors

Thermistors are semiconductors that show a large change in resistance with temperature. The standard operating temperature range is -55°C to 150°C with a resolution of ±0.5°C, although some devices have shown long-term stability up to 300°C.

There are two types according to a positive or negative response with respect to temperature, referred to as negative temperature coefficient (NTC) and positive temperature coefficient (PTC). A NTC thermistor shows very large negative temperature coefficients (4 to 5%/°C) compared to a PTC, and so is usually more suitable for precision measurement although the resistance change is nonlinear with temperature. NTC thermistors are stable and repeatable, physically small in size, and usually inexpensive especially when made in high volumes. A non-linear conversion is required to determine the temperature from the measured resistance. Thermistors require a power source to provide a current for a resistance reading. Special leads are not required to connect thermistors to instruments, and only two wires are necessary as they operate at very high resistance compared to the leads.

3.5.5 Fibre optic sensors

Fibre optic sensors are being used increasingly for measuring moderate temperatures in many civil engineering and building situations particularly where distributed temperature sensing is required, ie measurements along the length of the sensor, not just at one point as with thermocouples. Other advantages of optical fibres are immunity to electromagnetic influences including lightning, high sensitivity and greater stability than electrical-based sensors. Typically they have an accuracy of ±0.1°C.

Various types of fibre optic temperature sensor have been developed. Spot (single location) sensors measure the change in optical properties of a material that is very sensitive to temperature. For example, a thin film, typically gallium arsenide, is deposited on the end of an optical fibre and the temperature measured from the reflected absorption/transmission spectrum. Distributed sensors usually employ the fibre Bragg grating (FBG) method as described in Section 3.3.2.5.

3.5.6 Temperature sensors compared

The characteristics of the three main types of temperature sensor are listed in Table 3.6. The advice of manufacturers should be sought in selecting a sensor for a particular application (see Appendix A1.2 of DTI Report 1).

Table 3.6 *Characteristics of temperature sensors (courtesy Peak Sensors, UK)*

	Thermocouple	Resistance thermometer (RTD)	Thermistor
Accuracy	Less accurate	More accurate	Less accurate
Temperature range	-250°C to +2600°C	-200°C to +850°C	-60°C to +300°C
Stability (drift)	Reasonable for limited lifetime	Good	Good
Repeatability	Reasonable	Good	Good
Hysteresis	Excellent	Good	Good
Vibration	Very resistant	Less resistant	Good
Measurement area	Single Point	Whole RT element	Whole bead (small)
Diameter	Small sizes (to 0.25 mm)	Larger (3.0 mm min)	Small (0.5 mm min)
Linearity	Not linear	Linear	Not linear
Reference junction	Required	Not required	Not required
Lead wire resistance	No problem	Must be considered	No problem
Contact required	Yes	Yes	Yes
Response	Fast	Slower	Medium

3.6 CONCRETE MOISTURE STATE

3.6.1 Introduction

Water is an essential component of concrete. Early in the life of a concrete structure it is necessary for cement to hydrate in order for the concrete to develop strength and attain the required hardened state properties. Loss of moisture due to drying from concrete leads to shrinkage, which may result in shrinkage cracks. Penetration of water from an external source into hardened concrete is a necessary condition for damaging alkali aggregate reaction, freeze/thaw attack and delayed ettringite formation. External water may also bring with it chlorides (increasing the risk of reinforcement corrosion), sulphates (increasing the risk of sulphate attack) and other aggressive species. Water is involved in all major deterioration processes and so monitoring moisture in concrete structures generally helps in following and predicting degradation processes.

When concrete dries, water is first lost from the capillary pores, the spaces between the cement grains and aggregate particles not filled by hydration products. As drying continues water is lost from the gel pores within the hydration products. In partially dry concrete water is present as both liquid and vapour. Relative humidity is defined as the amount of water vapour in air relative to the amount it would contain if saturated, expressed as a percentage. Saturated air at a given temperature has a relative humidity of 100 per cent.

Most methods of measuring the moisture state of concrete are based on either measuring the relative humidity in a hole in the concrete (Section 3.6.2) or measuring a property of the concrete, most commonly electrical resistivity (Section 3.6.3), and relating this to the actual moisture content. Choice of whether to monitor relative humidity or moisture content will depend on what is more relevant to the objective of the monitoring. For example, the rate of carbonation is dependent upon relative humidity while the alkali silica reaction expansion is more closely related to moisture content. Concrete indicating 100 per cent relative humidity may be far from fully saturated with water and so at higher moisture contents it is more informative to monitor moisture content rather than relative humidity.

Most properties monitored to indicate moisture content are also affected by temperature, and so temperature is also frequently monitored (Section 3.5) to allow a correction to be made.

Details and manufacturer contacts for humidity and moisture sensors are given in the data sheets in Appendices A1.1 and A1.2 of DTI Report 1. Several of the case studies in Appendix A2.2 of DTI Report 1 include the monitoring of moisture, in particular to assist in interpreting corrosion monitoring measurements.

Permanent humidity and moisture content sensors usually need to be installed in holes (pre-formed or drilled) in concrete, where they can be placed at appropriate depths. The location of the holes needs to be selected carefully so as not to cause damage that may hasten the ingress of outside moisture and salts.

3.6.2 Humidity

3.6.2.1 *General*

Monitoring relative humidity is an attractive method for determining the moisture state of concrete because it does not involve contact with the concrete itself avoiding the potential problem of contamination from dissolved salts, which occurs with other methods.

Sensors for measuring humidity are referred to as hygrometers. There are several types including capacitance, resistance, dew point and electrochemical, with embedded optical fibre methods under development. Calibration of humidity sensors is important, and needs to be carried out periodically to ensure accurate readings.

3.6.2.2 *Capacitive sensor*

Capacitive hygrometers measure the change in dielectric constant between two electrodes embedded in a hygroscopic material that absorbs or releases moisture in proportion to the surrounding relative humidity. Materials used for the hygroscopic layer include polymer films, lithium chloride, an aqueous solution of hygroscopic salt, a carbon-powder suspension in gelatinous cellulose and aluminium oxide. Capacitive hygrometers can measure relative humidity over a wide range, generally from less than 10 per cent to over 98 per cent with an accuracy down to ±1 per cent, and have an operational temperature range typically of -40°C to +80°C.

Capacitive sensor designs are suitable for insertion into cavities in concrete and automated monitoring versions are available.

3.6.2.3 *Dew point sensor*

Dew point is directly related to relative humidity and is defined as the temperature to which air should be cooled, at constant barometric pressure, for water vapour to condense. The dew point is equal to the current temperature at 100 per cent relative humidity. Dew point decreases as the relative humidity decreases, given the same air temperature.

The two most widely used types of dew point sensor are the resistive sensor and the chilled mirror hygrometer. Resistive sensors are similar to capacitive sensors in that the dew point is measured by sensing water absorbance into a hygroscopic material. The conductance of the hygroscopic material increases as it absorbs moisture from the air, which causes additional current to run through wires in the sensor, heating the sensor to the equilibrium temperature at which the material again becomes non-conductive. The equilibrium temperature is measured by a temperature sensor and is converted into a dew point temperature based on a linear relationship.

The chilled mirror sensor is more complex and contains an ambient temperature sensor and a dew point sensing system with dew point temperature sensor and a cooling device. In taking a reading, the ambient and dew point temperatures are recorded and related to the relative humidity. The dew point is measured in a second air-pocket by controlled cooling, using an optical system to measure loss of light transmission from a chilled mirror as moisture forms. The complete sensor is contained in a housing suitable for insertion into a hole. Chilled mirror hygrometers are very accurate and typically can measure relative humidity from 40 to 90 per cent with an accuracy of better than ±1 per cent, and from 1 to 40 per cent to better than ±0.5 per cent. The long-term stability of a reference-grade chilled mirror hygrometer is excellent, with the temperature sensor changing as little as 0.01°C per yr, depending on the type and quality of temperature sensor used in the hygrometer.

Chilled mirror equipment is more complex and costly compared to other humidity sensors, and for this reason chilled mirror hygrometers are rarely used for measuring humidity in concrete. Chilled mirror hygrometers are used more often as a dew point reference standard for calibrating other humidity sensors because of their great accuracy. The polymer-based resistive relative humidity sensor by comparison is much less expensive, but covers a narrower range of humidity and although less precise is adequate and more widely used for a large range of day-to-day environmental measurements.

3.6.2.4 *Wood/brick resistance sensor*

Porous materials such as wood and brick absorb moisture from their environment and may be used as moisture/humidity sensors in concrete. A piece of the material is inserted into a hole in the concrete and the moisture content is determined by measuring the electrical resistance between two wire probes inserted into the material. Sensors of this type eliminate variations in the dielectric property of the concrete due to variations in pore solution composition so that variations in moisture state are isolated.

Wood sensors are inserted loosely into holes in concrete and measure the humidity of the surrounding air, which reflects that of the concrete. When used to measure moisture at depth, a plastic sleeve is inserted into the drilled hole and the space between the sleeve and concrete filled with epoxy, the end of the plastic tube is then pierced and the wood sensor is inserted. Wood sensors are typically 50 mm long by 10 mm in diameter, inexpensive, and offer long-term stability. Wires inserted into the wood enable the electrical resistance to be monitored remotely.

3.6.2.5 *Fibre optic sensor*

Fibre optic sensors for measuring humidity and moisture are being developed. Underlying principles used include the change in refractive index of a hygroscopic polymer coating on an optic fibre as it swells and the change in colour of a pH sensitive dye on the surface of a fibre as its moisture content varies.

3.6.3 Concrete resistivity

The electrical resistivity of concrete is highly dependent upon its moisture content. This is because electrical conduction in concrete is due to ion migration within the concrete pore solution - more pore solution results in more continuous flow paths and so more conduction. The type, size and arrangement of embedded electrodes for measuring resistivity and the measuring circuit were outlined in the context of measuring concrete resistivity to estimate corrosion rate (Section 3.4.3).

Unfortunately, concrete resistivity also depends on cement type, concrete mix proportions, concrete maturity, pore solution composition and temperature. Consequently there is no direct correlation between the measured resistance and the absolute percentage of moisture. In determining the moisture content, the electrical resistance is measured, the resistivity calculated and the moisture content determined either by given relationships or by specific correlations. An accurate measurement can only be achieved by calibrating the sensor in concrete of the same composition as that being monitored and by correcting for temperature variation. It should be recognised that if an external source of ions (eg seawater or de-icing salts) concentrates the pore solution, the resistivity will reduce, even though the moisture content may remain constant. Conversely, carbonation or exposure to fresh water will lead to a decrease in pore solution concentration and an increase in resistivity. The main attractions of the electrical resistivity method are that it provides an instant reading, large changes in resistivity generally indicate a change in moisture content and the electrodes are rugged and may be permanently embedded without requiring calibration.

3.7 CONCRETE CHEMISTRY

3.7.1 Introduction

Ideally it would be possible to remotely monitor the chemical composition of the solid and pore solution phases of concrete. Monitoring variations with depth would be helpful for following the progress of common deterioration processes. Sulphate content is critical to sulphate attack, alkali metals govern alkali aggregate reaction and chloride and pH levels control the initiation of reinforcement corrosion. pH reduction is also an indicator of leaching and acid attack. Calcium nitrite is used as a corrosion inhibiting admixture in concrete and there are concerns about its long-term effectiveness due to redistribution and leaching out in wetting and drying environments. The ability to monitor nitrite concentration at various depths into the concrete would address this concern.

Ion-selective electrodes are used routinely for measuring a wide range of ions in aqueous solutions in industrial processes and for environmental monitoring. Automated monitoring of water quality is feasible with ion selective electrodes that can be periodically removed and recalibrated. However, automated monitoring of the composition of concrete is a far greater challenge. Concrete structures typically have design lives of 50 to 120 years and in some cases longer. Once a sensor is embedded in concrete it cannot be removed for servicing or calibration. Even in the case of retrofitted systems, electrodes are difficult to remove without damage because they are grouted in place to achieve good electrolytic contact with the concrete pore solution. Many of the environments in which reinforced concrete degrades involve wetting and drying cycles that may cause sensors to dry out for long periods. This is another major problem for most ion selective electrodes.

Several research groups are working on producing chemical sensors for monitoring concrete structures. Considering the widespread and costly nature of reinforcement corrosion, most effort has been directed at trying to develop sensors to measure chloride concentration and pH. However, to date there are no independent reports of successful long-term monitoring of any aspect of the chemistry of concrete using embedded sensors. The information that follows concerning the monitoring of chloride concentration and pH originates from research programmes rather than successful field implementation.

3.7.2 Chloride

Chloride ions may initiate the corrosion of reinforcing steel in concrete and so there is considerable interest in being able to measure chloride levels, especially for structures exposed to sea-water or de-icing salts. It is not sufficient to measure chloride at or near the concrete surface, because their levels and profile deeper within the concrete cover are more important. So there is a need to embed or insert sensors in concrete, down to the level of the reinforcing steel.

The only ion selective electrode now used for monitoring chloride in concrete is the silver/silver chloride electrode. It is also widely used as a reference electrode for measuring half cell potential in concrete, especially in relation to linear polarisation resistance measurements, cathodic protection and potential mapping. The potential of a silver/silver chloride electrode varies only slightly (typically 20 or 30mV) with the chloride level. This is attractive for general use as a reference electrode because the change with chloride ion does not mask the moderate to large changes in electrode potential of interest in applications such as cathodic protection and potential monitoring. However, sensitive instrumentation can detect and quantify the potential change due to chloride.

A silver/silver chloride electrode suitable for embedding in concrete for monitoring chloride level is simple in design. It consists of a cell containing a silver chloride electrolyte solution in which a silver wire is immersed, with a porous plug at the bottom, which is in electrical contact with the concrete through which ion interchange occurs. In operation, a small amount of electrolyte leaks out of the porous membrane and mixes with moisture in the adjacent concrete to complete an electrical circuit. To reduce drying out of the electrolyte when the electrode is used for long-term, unattended monitoring, the silver chloride solution is present in gel form and contains an anti-drying agent.

Various investigators have examined the use of directly embedded Ag/AgCl electrodes for measuring chloride in concrete. Climent-Llorca *et al* (1996) embedded silver wires coated with silver chloride in concrete, and concluded that the electrodes were suitable for measuring chloride in the short-term (three months), but that in long-term tests they may give ambiguous results. Elsener *et al* (1997) also report the development of a silver/silver chloride electrode consisting of a silver wire coated with silver chloride, which is embedded directly in concrete. The electrode has shown good long-term stability and reproducibility in laboratory testing and forms part of the ECI-1 corrosion sensor from Virginia Technologies (USA).

Optical fibre sensors are under development for measuring chlorides in concrete, and most are based on measuring changes in light absorption of a chemically sensitive coating. Fibre optic sensors have been installed to monitor chlorides in bridges in Missouri, USA (DTI Report 1 Case study 29), but no results have been reported since installation.

3.7.3 pH

The high pH of concrete is the basis of its ability to protect steel reinforcement from corrosion. pH may be reduced by carbonation, leaching or acid attack.

A hydrogen electrode is widely used for measuring pH in laboratory analysis, and is usually combined with a reference electrode. In the hydrogen pH electrode, electrolyte from the reference electrode leaks out of a liquid junction to mix with the solution being measured to complete an electrical circuit. The combined solution gives an ionic charge that is measured by the glass hydrogen electrode to give a pH value. The electrode and bulbous porous sensing area are made from fragile glass and have to be kept continually wet, so are unsuitable for embedding in concrete.

The more recent development of solid state pH electrodes (termed ion sensitive field effect transistors or ISFET electrodes), may offer some possibility for measuring pH in concrete. An ISFET electrode is housed in a plastic or steel cartridge-type casing, and so is more robust than a glass pH electrode. The sensor at the tip of the electrode is small and consists of a silicon semiconductor substrate covered with a silicon electrical insulator that is only permeable to hydrogen ions. Hydrogen ions at or near the surface of the insulator will cause a variable voltage potential between the insulator and the underlying semiconductor material, which is proportional to the relative concentration of hydrogen ions in the sample solution. ISFET electrodes can measure pH by direct insertion in aqueous systems and semi-solid materials including soils. In some situations it may be possible to design a housing to hold the electrode in a closely fitting wetted cavity in concrete. Particular advantages of ISFET electrodes are the ability to survive wet and dry conditions, and the minute drop of material needed to measure pH.

The development of pH sensors for use in concrete based on a dye-impregnated gel or sol-gel attached to the end or side of an optic fibre is being investigated at various institutions.

Again, it should be emphasised that to date there have been no independent reports of successful long-term monitoring of any aspect of the chemistry of concrete, including pH, using embedded sensors.

3.8 EXPOSURE ENVIRONMENT

3.8.1 Introduction

The deterioration of concrete is almost entirely due to external environmental factors, with water playing an essential role. For example, the conventional and thaumasite forms of sulphate attack require an external sulphate solution (usually groundwater), alkali silica reaction and freeze/thaw attack require an external source of water and reinforcement corrosion is initiated by atmospheric carbonation or chloride penetration, usually from sea-water or de-icing salts. The rate of penetration of aggressive species and the rate of their reactions with concrete phases will depend on, among other factors, their concentration and temperature. The moisture state at the surface of the concrete is usually important too and this is controlled by groundwater (or sea-water) level, ambient relative humidity, wind direction and velocity and rainfall. In some situations redox potential and the presence of stray currents are important, and so knowledge of the nature of the surrounding external environment is important to understanding behaviour and predicting future performance. Unsurprisingly, life prediction models usually involve environmental aspects of the exposure environment as inputs. Sometimes these values are known and there is no need to monitor them.

For example, the chloride content of sea-water is effectively constant and would not be expected to change over the life of a concrete structure and so a textbook value can usually be adopted. In other situations environmental parameters vary with time and cannot be reliably predicted so it may be advantageous to monitor them. This is especially true where it is expected that micro-climates will exist around a structure, for example the humidity and temperature will vary around a building according to the compass bearing, prevailing wind direction and degree of sheltering.

Methods for monitoring environmental variables of relevance to the performance of concrete structures are summarised in Table 3.7.

Table 3.7 *Main measurement methods applicable to the remote monitoring of variables in water, soil and air environments*

Environment	Measured variable	Monitoring method
Groundwater, waste water	pH	pH electrode
	Temperature	Thermocouples, thermistors
	Ions	Ion selective electrodes
	Water pressure	Piezometer
	Redox potential	Electrodes
Soil	Resistivity	Electrical resistivity
	Stray dc currents	Potential
	Potential	Reference electrodes
	Water, moisture	TDR, capacitance sensors
	Soil pressure	Piezometer
Air	Rainfall	Rain gauge
	Relative humidity	Hygrometer
	Wind	Anemometer
	Gases (eg SO_2)	Gas sensors
	Temperature	Thermocouples, thermistors

Each environment presents a different challenge to monitoring. A detailed description of the methods available for monitoring environmental variables is beyond the scope of this guide. The purpose of this section is to present a broad approach to the subject, indicating the possibilities available. Equipment covering the environmental field is listed in Appendix A2.1 of DTI Report 1.

3.8.2 Water and soil

It is generally the water in soil (ie the groundwater) that is of interest with regard to the degradation of concrete structures, rather than the solid components of soil, because the groundwater carries dissolved salts, is mobile and is available to attack concrete. So in this section, water and soil are considered together. The properties of water and groundwater in soil that are relevant to the degradation of concrete structures such a dams, storage tanks, tunnels, offshore structures, bridge piers, basements and foundations are pH, water level, water pressure, water flow, temperature, dissolved gas (including oxygen) concentrations, dissolved salt (including chloride and sulphate) concentrations, stray currents, soil moisture content and electrical resistivity.

A remote water monitoring system comprises distinct units, most available off the shelf, such as a water sampler, analytical instrumentation, process control equipment linking sampled water and analytical instrumentation, data logger to store data (can also programme sampling and analysis sequencing if necessary), data transmission system (telemetry or cable), computer interface and monitoring software. A brief description of sampling technology and methods of analysis in the context of a remote monitoring system follows. Equipment and instrumentation manufacturers are listed in Appendix A1.2 of DTI Report 1.

Completely automated, portable or permanent sampling systems are widely available. Sampling systems provide a wide range of operational possibilities, such as in-line analysis or collection then analysis, with dumping or collection of samples, sample collection over a period of months for laboratory analysis, single, multiple or composite sampling, heating or cooling to prevent sample degradation etc. Power for sampling systems can be a combination of cable, battery, wind or solar power.

Analytical instrumentation and control technology is available for monitoring and measuring most chemicals and physical environmental variables remotely in the field. Temperature, redox potential, pH and a range of ions (such as chloride and sulphide) using ion selective electrodes are commonly monitored remotely, for example as part of water and environmental monitoring programmes. Some monitoring systems are available that can perform laboratory type chemical analysis on-site automatically, for example for nitrate, phosphate and ammonium.

Moisture is widely monitored in the agricultural industry so the technology for measuring moisture or groundwater in soils is well developed. Most of the techniques used for monitoring moisture in concrete remotely (Section 3.6) are also applied to soils, time domain reflectometry (TDR) and tensiometers are also commonly used. TDR measures the velocity of an electromagnetic wave travelling through a transmission line. The velocity is related to the dielectric constant of the soil between the conductors of the transmission line, which in turn is related to moisture content of the soil. Sensors are little affected by salinity in the soil (except at high salt concentrations) and are easily automated for remote monitoring. Tensiometers measure the tension with which soils hold water, can be automated and are not affected by salinity in soils. They consist of a long tube with a porous plug at the bottom, which is inserted into the soil. The tube is filled with water and the vacuum created by water being drawn into the soil measured and quantified.

Commercial soil moisture monitors frequently measure other variables such as temperature, conductivity, and salinity. Many equipment manufactures supply complete sensor-data logging- transmission systems, but all moisture sensors can be easily linked into commonly available data logging and transmission systems. Appendix A1.2 of DTI Report 1 lists manufacturers of water and soil monitoring equipment.

3.8.3 Air

The variables in air that are relevant to the degradation of concrete structures include rainfall, humidity, temperature, wind and industrial contaminants such as acidic gases. Monitoring wind is important in assessing the safety of large exposed structures such as bridges and tall buildings. Monitoring temperature and relative humidity is relevant in checking for freeze/thaw conditions that can lead to damage to roads and many structures. The corrosiveness of air towards reinforced concrete is strongly influenced by relative humidity and the concentration of pollutants in the air such as chlorides and sulphur dioxide. Air pollutants that increase the acidity of dew or rainfall will attack concrete.

The remote and automated monitoring of weather is a well developed science and the technology and instrumentation available will not be discussed in detail here. Remotely located instrumentation to monitor industrial waste gases directly such as sulphur and nitrogen oxides, hydrogen sulphide and ammonia is widely available and employed. Suppliers of weather and industrial gas monitoring equipment are listed in Appendix A1.2 of DTI Report 1.

3.8.4 Earthquake

Earthquakes can cause widespread and severe damage to concrete structures, their total destructive capability depending on the size of the earthquake. Seismometers are installed in the ground to measure earthquake magnitude and pin-point the location of the epicentre below the surface. Accelerometers are placed on structures to measure the acceleration due to the earthquake movement (3.3.6). Earthquake monitoring systems are widely installed in earthquake prone areas, such as California and Japan, to provide early warning.

3.9 DATA MANAGEMENT

3.9.1 Introduction

The conventional approach in structural health monitoring, still widely used, is to run cables between the sensors on the structure to a centralised data collection system. The data is downloaded periodically by staff visiting the site, followed by computer analysis and decision-making. The disadvantages of this approach include installation of cabling is time consuming, expensive and may cause damage to the structure, cable degradation occurs with time, electromagnetic interference, maintenance becomes expensive and periodic data reading may miss important events.

The conventional approach is rapidly changing as advances in technology provide greater flexibility and new opportunities for monitoring system design. Data is increasingly being transmitted using existing telephone lines over the internet to a remote computer and, where possible, the trend now is to connect sensors by wireless to on-site data loggers and to transmit the data via cellular phones or satellite to remote computers.

The basic functioning of remote monitoring systems is discussed briefly in the following sections. The interested reader is referred to the manufacturers for detailed information and advice on instrumentation available, the design and installation of monitoring systems and ancillary equipment.

3.9.2 Data logging

A data logger is an electronic device that records measurements with time (on/off, open/closed, voltage, temperature, pressure, relative humidity, light intensity and events). Most are connected by wire to sensors, but wireless data loggers are now available. Data loggers may be battery or cable-powered and are equipped with a microprocessor, signal conditioning electronics, clock and data storage. Some may also have sensors included. Significant developments in low power electronics and battery technology have enabled manufacturers to design much smaller portable data loggers. They are usually programmed through a personal computer using software to set measurement times/intervals, processing algorithms (outputting results in the desired units) and to allow the collected data to be viewed. The instruction sets also allow for triggered output, for example if a bridge is being monitored, data collection can be triggered by a sensor detecting the approach of a car or an earthquake.

Basic systems have a few channels, more sophisticated expandable systems measure hundreds. The total logging time is a function of the recording rate and internal memory. To conserve battery life, loggers use special low power electronics and are programmed to sleep and only wake to measure and record at discrete pre-set periods. Data loggers not only provide advanced measurement capabilities, but can also control external devices to sound alarms, actuate electrical devices, or shut down equipment. Voice-synthesised modems are available, so the system can actually contact and inform an operator exactly what is happening.

The use of wireless data loggers has advantages as there are no cables to run, which eliminates the risk of electrical faults or lightning surges feeding round a system, temporary deployments are practical, there is no damage to structures. De-briefing of the logger can be achieved by a variety of media, including GSM dial, PSTN dial, SMS text, and email.

Data loggers are not always needed, and can be bypassed by sending a wireless signal directly from the sensor to the receiver-computer station.

Examples of the practical application of data loggers are given in Appendices A1 and A2 of DTI Report 1.

3.9.3 Data transmission

Data can be transferred from data loggers to a remote computer by various means including wire, wireless, satellite, optical and cellular phone or a combination of these. The world is seeing a rapid shift from wired to wireless communications, as shown by the growth in the personal mobile phone market.

The telecommunications field can be confusing because of the wide range of transmitting options, technology and standards available, and not least the abbreviated terminology (acronyms) used. The basics of data transmission technology as they relate to industrial monitoring situations will be reviewed briefly here. The reader is referred to the manufacturers listed in Appendix A1.2 of DTI Report 1 for more information on data transmission systems.

The use of copper wire cables to connect sensors to data loggers and by phone line to a remote computer using Ethernet, ModBus or RS-232 links is still the most widely used method of data transmission in structural condition monitoring systems. Fibre optic cables also find use for data transmission, especially for fibre optic-based sensors.

While the use of wireless connection and data transfer is likely to replace wire cables in many situations, wired connections do have advantages such as faster and higher data transfer rates, greater reliability over distances of up to 1 km, no line-of-sight restriction, which is a potential problem for wireless transmission, and the existence of a comprehensive, network of cabled phone lines (wire and fibre optic). The decline in the use of wired communications is largely due to improvements in wireless technology, resulting in lowered costs and improved dependability.

The telemetry options available for use in monitoring civil engineering structures depend on the application, in particular the transmitting distance required, remoteness of the structure, power availability, data transfer rate, data reliability, and interference limitations. Short distance telemetry is suitable for monitoring sensors on the structure itself, but long distance telemetry is required to transmit data over longer distances direct to dedicated server-linked computers via wireless modems, or using cellular or satellite systems.

A typical sensor wireless system might comprise sensors on a structure sending data via wireless transmission to a data logger located near the structure (within say 1 km), and from the data logger by landline, wireless (generally up to about 10 km range), cellular phone (GSM) or satellite (GPS) to a remote computer base station for analysis.

The main factors that have accelerated the usage of wireless data transfer include improvements in digital signal processing, and new standards such as the IEEE 802.11, the Wireless Application Protocol (WAP) and Bluetooth. Other advantages of wireless over wired data transmission are:

- significant reduction in cost and time otherwise required in Ethernet cabling sensors on a structure
- allows installation of sensors in inaccessible locations on a structure
- less damage to structure being monitored since installation fittings reduced
- sensors can be easily moved around the structure
- greater flexibility to share and extend the cable/DSL (digital subscriber line)/phone connection anywhere
- mobility, allowing access from remote devices such as laptop or PDA from home, office or site
- improved efficiency by sharing computer peripherals and data files from anywhere within a wireless network
- less susceptibility to damage from lightning, fire, vandalism, and accidents because little cabling involved.

Wireless transmission is restricted to specific radio wavelengths, as follows:

- microwave radio - signals are transmitted at high frequencies (eg 2.4 GHz) using parabolic dishes installed on towers or on the tops of buildings. Includes Bluetooth and WiFi protocols. This is the frequency that most wireless sensor networks now use. Disadvantages of microwave communication are limited transmission distance and susceptibility to interruption due to misalignment and/or atmospheric conditions
- VHF/UHF radio - electromagnetic transmission with frequencies of between 150 and 900 MHz. Special antennas are required to receive these signals
- spread spectrum radio – covering the frequency band 900 MHz to 5.8 GHz and free for general pubic use. Spread spectrum radio modems are used to ensure efficient network communication, including direct sequence spread spectrum (transmission on many frequencies at same time) or frequency hopping spread spectrum (transmission frequency changed periodically). Used by cellular/mobile phone network.

Fundamentally, the transmission distance increases as the wavelength decreases. High (microwave) frequency protocols such as Bluetooth and WiFi, operating respectively in the 2.4–2.485 GHz and 2.4 – 5.8 GHz range, are suitable for short distance transmission (15 m for Bluetooth, 100 m for WiFi, the IEEE 802.11 standard for LAN wireless protocols, commonly referred to as wireless Ethernet or Wireless LAN), have higher power requirements and may be subject to interference. The standards available for short-range wireless transmission systems are summarised in Table 3.8.

Table 3.8 *Standards for short-range wireless transmission*

	ZigBee 802.15.4	Bluetooth 802.15.1	WiFi 802.11b	GPRS/GSM 1XRTT/CDMA
System resource	4-32 kb	250 kb+	1 mb ±	16 mb+
Battery life (days)	100-1000+	1-7	0.1-5	1-7
Nodes per network	255/65 000+	7	30	1-1000
Bandwidth (KBps)	20-250	720	11 000+	64-128
Range (meters)	1-75+	1-10+	1-100	Kms
Application focus	Monitoring and control	Cable replacement	Web, email	Wireless voice and data
Advantages	□ reliable, secure networking □ protocol simplicity □ low power consumption.	□ low incremental cost □ ease of use/ convenience □ moderate data rate.	□ high data throughput □ flexibility (work and home) □ hot spot connectivity.	□ broad geographic coverage.

Lower frequencies in the HF/VHF wireless bands allow greater transmission distances than in the microwave frequencies, but the use of high powered transmitters or satellite communication equipment is required for distances over about 20 km. The transmitting distance and power requirements of useable HF/VHF wireless bands are given in Table 3.9. These lower frequencies are potentially affected by regulatory restrictions.

Wireless transmission of data is less susceptible to interruption by electromagnetic interference (EMI) than wired transmission. For example, power generating stations use wireless communication to monitor generating equipment and switching systems in high-EMI areas within plants. Digital signals are less susceptible to interference than analogue signals.

Table 3.9 *Frequencies and transmission ranges for the more popular European licence-free wireless bands*

Frequency (MHz) (country)	Permitted output power (mW)	Practical range, 3 m above ground level
173 (UK, IE)	10	500 m to 10 km (20 km or above with FFSK version)
150 to 225 licensed	10 to 5000	Up to 50 km using FFSK modulation at 500 mW (licence required)
433-434 (all)	10	100m to 300 m WBFM or 100 m to 2 km NBFM
458 (UK, IE, DE)	500	500 m to 30 km
868-870 (all)	5	30 m to 150 m
869.5 (all)	500	500 m to 15 km
869.5 and LBT	5/25	10 m to 100 m is the intended range as this is a local sensor interface standard protocol and not intended for long distance links

Wired systems are generally more secure than wireless systems because radio transmissions on all wavelengths can be picked up using commonly available scanners. Spread spectrum wireless transmission in which the frequency used is changed frequently can overcome this problem largely, and other options include transmission encryption, encoding, and interleaving. Unauthorised tapping of wireless transmissions, however, is not a major concern in the monitoring of structures, unless it leads to data corruption.

3.9.4 Computer software

Transmission equipment, data loggers and certain types of sensors are provided with computer software by the equipment manufacturer. Manufacturers are usually prepared to customise software as required. Consult Appendix A1.2 of DTI Report 1 for manufacturer contact details.

3.9.5 Integrated automated monitoring systems

Remote monitoring systems vary in complexity in terms of the number of sensors, data capture and transfer system, computer analysis and alarm system, but the basic architecture of a remote monitoring system remains the same. Wireless technology makes it easier to install single sensors or temporary sensing systems on structures quickly, without the cost and time limitation of having to run cables over the structure and the need to access cabled power. Battery power with solar power re-charging provides added flexibility to quickly install monitoring systems.

A large amount of data can be generated by an automated system and accessing this data, carrying out data reduction, pre-analysis and data access are all critical. Options include downloading data on demand, automated downloading and automatic posting to a web server. Systems for data reduction are also important, which are mainly aimed at trend analysis (in many cases signal change is more instructive than absolute values).

Organisational procedures need to be put in place to ensure that data is managed in a continuous way through the life of the system, ie:

- data is collected and reviewed regularly
- the system is maintained
- the system is designed to report when deviations from expected trends occur
- an action system is in place to investigate unusual events.

A degree of future proofing is also required to ensure that data collected now will still be accessible in 50 years time.

The design of a monitoring system is specific to a particular structure and the objectives of the monitoring. Section 3.2 presents key issues regarding specifying and commissioning monitoring systems. The case studies in Chapter 5 of this guide and Appendix A2.2 of DTI Report 1 illustrate the range of options and complexity of monitoring systems available.

4 Predicting remaining life based on monitoring data

4.1 INTRODUCTION

In this chapter the role of automated monitoring in the service life prediction of reinforced concrete structures is assessed. Numerous models covering a wide range of degradation mechanisms are reviewed and the possibility of obtaining the required input parameters from sensors installed in concrete elements is discussed. The most promising techniques for use in combination with automated monitoring are highlighted. The application of sensor data within the context of probabilistic analysis is also considered. Data obtained from automated monitoring is ideal for use in conjunction with statistical techniques such as Bayesian updating and spatial analysis.

For a detailed analysis of all the topics covered in this chapter refer to DTI Report 2.

4.1.1 Deterioration mechanisms considered

Table 4.1 indicates the deterioration mechanisms most commonly critical (ie controlling service life) for different types of structure. It is important to recognise that these deterioration mechanisms are highly dependant on specific exposure environments. For example, freeze/thaw damage only becomes an issue when near saturated concrete is subject to sub-zero temperatures. Alkali aggregate reaction is detectable in many structures but only becomes significant when high alkali contents, particular contents of reactive minerals in the aggregate and moist conditions are all present and there is insufficient reinforcement to contain the expansions. Often different deterioration processes interact in structures (eg reinforcement corrosion, freeze/thaw action and abrasion in car parks). There are also some less commonly encountered chemical deterioration processes associated with exposure to other substances aggressive to concrete including acids, ammonium salts and milk.

Table 4.1 *Predominant deterioration mechanisms for different types of structure*

Type of structure	Corrosion			Freeze/ thaw	Alkali aggregate reaction	Sulphate attack	Leaching	Abrasion	Acid Attack
	Chloride-induced	CO_2-induced	Biological activity						
Above ground buildings	light grey	dark grey			light grey				
Bridges	dark grey	light grey		light grey	light grey	light grey			
Foundations			light grey		light grey	light grey			
Marine structures	dark grey		light grey	light grey	light grey		light grey	light grey	
Dams				light grey	light grey		light grey		
Tunnels	dark grey	light grey	light grey		light grey	light grey			
Tanks and pipes	light grey	light grey	light grey		light grey	light grey	light grey		light grey
Industrial floors		light grey						dark grey	light grey

Note
Shading: commonly affected (dark grey), sometimes affected (light grey), uncommon (no shading)

All degradation mechanisms listed in Table 4.1 are considered in this guide with the exception of biological activity leading to reinforcement corrosion. Biological attack is rarely observed in concrete structures so it has not been the focus of much research. No viable service life models for this deterioration process have been identified.

The critical limit states corresponding to reinforcement corrosion, freeze-thaw attack, sulphate attack and alkali-aggregate reaction have already been introduced in Section 2.3. More detailed discussion on the specification of critical limit states for all the degradation mechanisms is presented in the following sections.

4.1.2 Availability of service life models

Table 4.2 gives an overall view of the availability of service life models according to the deterioration process and the limit state of interest.

Table 4.2 *Availability of service life models*

Deterioration process	Serviceability limit state	Ultimate limit state
Reinforcement corrosion	Corrosion initiation	Flexural failure
	Cover cracking	Shear failure
	Spalling	Anchorage failure
	Excessive crack widths	
	Excessive deflections	
Alkali aggregate reaction	Cover cracking	Degradation of mechanical properties
	Spalling	
Sulphate attack	Cover cracking	Degradation of mechanical properties
	Spalling	
Freeze-thaw attack	Cover cracking	Degradation of mechanical properties
	Spalling	
Leaching	Loss of alkalinity at depth of rebar	Degradation of mechanical properties
Acid attack	Loss of alkalinity at depth of rebar	Degradation of mechanical properties
Abrasion	Loss of cover	

Note
Shading: models widely available (dark grey), limited modelling (light grey), no models available (no shading)

Reinforcement corrosion is the most frequently observed cause of deterioration in concrete structures and so there is more research interest in this field. It may be regarded as a two stage process consisting of an initiation phase and a propagation phase. The former represents the time to the onset of corrosion due to the ingress of chloride ions or the penetration of the carbonation front into concrete. The latter is concerned with the loss of steel cross-sectional area and the detrimental effect this has on the structural performance of concrete elements.

The majority of service life models developed attempt to predict the duration of the initiation phase. In comparison, much less work has been carried out on analysing structural behaviour during the propagation phase. The models available for estimating the time to cover cracking, loss of steel-concrete bond and the associated affect on the load bearing capacity of damaged members suffer from severe limitations arising from simplified boundary conditions assumed in the analysis and the difficulty in obtaining some of the input parameters required. Serviceability criteria such as excessive deflections and crack widths may prove to be the critical limit states with regards to the in-service behaviour of damaged elements. However very few models are available capable of predicting the full load-deflection history of a corroding beam while only one has been found to analyze the occurrence of excessive crack widths as a consequence of expansion of the corrosion products. Surprisingly no models are available now to predict the time to corrosion induced spalling of the concrete cover even though much of the published literature cites this event as a major limit state.

The lack of viable service life models is even more evident when considering deterioration processes that directly affect the concrete independent of the reinforcement such as sulphate attack, freeze-thaw attack and alkali-aggregate reaction. This is primarily attributed to the degree of complexity associated with the underlying chemical and physical processes taking place rendering the degradation mechanisms intractable to describe within a mathematical framework. In some cases where models have been developed, the focus is on predicting changes in concrete properties, such as porosity, or the internal stress state generated as a result of the continuing deterioration process. However the models fail to specify appropriate failure criterion by which to determine when the concrete is deemed unfit for purpose so their use in service life estimation is limited.

It is important to note that all the service life models reviewed consider the occurrence of a given deterioration process in isolation. The interaction between degradation processes, for example the diffusion of chloride ions and the ingress of the carbonation front, is rarely taken into account. There is clearly a need for service life models encompassing the action of more than one deterioration mechanism.

Much work is yet to be done to provide a comprehensive set of service life models capable of representing the complete behaviour of reinforced concrete elements subject to deterioration.

4.2 SUITABILITY OF MODELS FOR USE WITH AUTOMATED MONITORING

To assess whether a given service life model is suitable for use in combination with automated monitoring, it is helpful to classify service life models into four main categories. These are:

1. Empirical models.
2. Analytical models.
3. Numerical models.
4. Models based on detecting changes in the chemical and physical behaviour of concrete.

The nature of any given model dictates the extent to which automated monitoring can take an active role in the assessment process. Each model type is discussed below.

Empirical models – Not suitable for use with automated monitoring:

Empirical models are not concerned with describing the actual degradation mechanisms in a mathematical context. They provide simple equations that are easy to apply. The model parameters are obtained from regression analysis of laboratory or field exposure data so are highly specific to the experimental conditions. Their application in general situations with varying boundary conditions is questionable. Empirical models provide no potential for the use of automated monitoring.

Analytical models – Extremely limited use with automated monitoring:

Analytical solutions provide closed-form solutions to analyse the degradation of concrete by solving the governing partial differential equations based on simplified assumptions regarding the material properties and environmental conditions. The models are relatively straightforward and suitable for use in practice. However they are rigid and inflexible in format and the validity of the predictions for atypical circumstances is questionable as the models do not describe the underlying physical and chemical processes taking place within concrete. The input parameters are usually determined from laboratory or field tests. The application of analytical models in conjunction with automated monitoring is extremely limited. The main advantages and limitations of the analytical approach can best be illustrated by considering the solution to Fick's second law of diffusion describing the diffusion of a contaminant in a medium.

Diffusion is described mathematically according to Fick's second law (the rate of transfer of the diffusing substance through a plane of unit area is proportional to the concentration gradient measured normal to the plane) as:

$$\frac{\partial C}{\partial t} = D\frac{\partial^2 C}{\partial x^2} \tag{4.1}$$

where C is the concentration of the diffusing substance at a distance x from the surface and time t and D is the diffusion coefficient for the process.

An analytical solution to Fick's second law of diffusion in one dimension can be obtained for the case of a semi-infinite medium assuming that the concentration of the diffusing substance at the exterior surface is constant. The analytical solution is:

$$C(x,t) = C_s\left[1 - erf\left(\frac{x}{2\sqrt{Dt}}\right)\right] \tag{4.2}$$

where C_s is the concentration of the contaminant at the surface and erf is the error function. Equation 4.2 is the equation that has been most widely used to model chloride penetration into concrete. It is relatively simple to use, but its accuracy is limited by the assumptions made in its derivation.

For example it is assumed that the diffusion coefficient D is constant and does not vary with location and time, the surface concentration of contaminant C_s is constant and that diffusion is the sole transport mechanism. Clearly such assumptions are not valid when considering the penetration of contaminants, such as chloride ions, into concrete. Attempts have been made to overcome some of these limitations. For example, there have been modified solutions that incorporate the time-dependent nature of the chloride ion diffusion coefficient in concrete. This involves defining the diffusion equation in terms of a new time-invariant variable but this further complicates the solution. Neither of the parameters D or C_s can be obtained directly using embedded sensors.

Numerical models – potential for use with automated monitoring:

Numerical models are complex in nature as they try to describe the actual chemical and physical processes taking place in concrete within a mathematical framework. The solution procedure involves solving the governing partial differential equations using finite difference or finite element methods over the spatial domain considered at discrete time intervals. Numerical models usually consist of a large number of input parameters not all of which can be readily obtained. However they do provide a greater possibility of utilising data gathered from automated monitoring. The data can be used to update model input parameters at each time step in the calculation.

The benefits of the numerical approach over analytical techniques can be highlighted by again considering Fick's second law of diffusion. Equation 4.1 can be solved numerically using finite difference methods. This approach involves subdividing the solution domain into a grid of discrete points or nodes. The partial differential equation is written for each node and its derivatives replaced by finite-divided differences. This approach offers far greater freedom with regards to the specification of boundary conditions and assumptions made in the analysis. Both the spatial and time dependency of the diffusion coefficient D and the surface concentration of the contaminant C_s can be considered in the analysis. Also if the original governing partial differential equation, Equation 4.1, is suitably modified, the contribution of other transport mechanisms can be included in the analysis. So the numerical method enables a much more realistic model of the system under consideration to be formulated. However, this comes at a price, which is that many more input variables are required by such models.

Monitoring the behaviour of concrete – Suited for use with automated monitoring:

Service life models most suited for use in combination with automated monitoring are those that monitor chemical and physical changes occurring directly as a consequence of the degradation mechanism under consideration such as the propagation of the corrosion front towards the reinforcement (see Section 4.3.6.1) or the expansive stresses induced within concrete due to the formation of deleterious products (see Sections 4.4.5 and 4.5.5). Generally these models require relatively few input parameters, the most critical of which can be measured using sensors embedded in the structure at various locations and depths.

These techniques have considerable advantages over the traditional approach to service life prediction. They remove the need for mathematical models that analyse the complex chemical and physical processes actually taking place within the concrete. Inaccuracies arising from simplified boundary conditions are avoided. The number of input parameters required is significantly reduced. The reliability of residual life estimates are improved as they are determined from a consideration of the observed in-service behaviour of the structure. This is all achieved by placing intelligent monitoring at the centre of the durability assessment process.

4.3 REINFORCING STEEL CORROSION INITIATION

4.3.1 Introduction

Over the past several decades the corrosion of reinforcement in concrete has been identified as the primary cause of deterioration in concrete structures. The increased incidence of reinforcement corrosion is primarily due to the more severe environmental conditions that structures are now exposed to. For example the greater application of de-icing salts on bridges during winter periods and a rise in the number of concrete structures situated in close proximity to coastal regions.

Following the onset of corrosion, if no remedial measures are undertaken, the resulting increase in volume associated with the formation of corrosion products will eventually lead to spalling of the concrete cover, exposing the steel reinforcement. The subsequent reduction in bond between the steel and concrete and the loss of cross-sectional area of the reinforcement will, in time, adversely affect the serviceability and load capacity of reinforced concrete elements.

The total service life of reinforced concrete structures subject to reinforcement corrosion is commonly modelled as a two stage process consisting of an initiation period and a propagation period. The initiation period is defined as the time taken to the onset of reinforcement corrosion and is considered in this section. This is followed by the propagation period, which is defined as the time taken to reach specified serviceability or ultimate limit states and is considered in Section 4.4.

4.3.2 Corrosion initiation

Under normal environmental conditions reinforcement bars within concrete structures do not corrode. This is primarily due to the formation of a thin passive layer on the surface of the reinforcement, which renders the metal electrochemically inactive. The passive film acts as a protective layer preventing direct contact between the steel, oxygen and water. However the stability of this passivating film can be compromised in the presence of sufficiently high concentrations of chloride ions, defined as the chloride threshold level C_{th}, or as a result of a reduction in the pH of the concrete pore solution due to carbonation.

4.3.3 Chloride penetration into concrete

The ingress of chloride ions into concrete is a complex process. The main two transport mechanisms are diffusion, which is the movement of ions under a concentration gradient, and advection, which is the flow of water under a pressure gradient, due to capillary suction or an external head of water. Note that all concrete as cast contains some background chlorides. Before circa 1970 it was common to use CaCl as an accelerator, which often gave initial chloride contents high enough to initiate corrosion. Establishing the as-built background chloride concentration is an essential precursor of any modelling of chloride ingress and corrosion initiation.

For concrete under saturated conditions, diffusion is the dominant transport mechanism. Diffusion of chloride ions in concrete takes place in the pore solution. The rate of diffusion is influenced by several factors. Concretes with high water-binder ratios are relatively porous with an extensively interconnected pore structure, and so they have correspondingly higher diffusion rates than concretes with low water-binder ratios. The continuous hydration of the cement and the associated changes in the size distribution and continuity of pores results in a reduction in diffusion rate with time. The inclusion of some mineral additions, such as blast furnace slag, pfa, and silica fume, can significantly reduce the rate of diffusion. With silica fume this improvement occurs rapidly and then stops, with slag and pfa there is a long-term improvement year by year. Temperature affects the rate of chloride ingress, with an increase in temperature resulting in a corresponding increase in the diffusion rate. The diffusion of chloride ions in concrete is also a function of the moisture content. As concrete dries out, there is a reduction in the size and number of continuous water paths. This means that diffusion reduces with decreasing moisture content and is negligible below a critical moisture level.

For reinforced concrete structures that are unsaturated and are subjected to wet and dry cycles, such as highway bridges and structures in a marine splash zone, advection is the dominant transport mechanism. In such cases the absorption of water is driven by capillary absorption and has a significant affect on chloride ion ingress. The rate of capillary suction is a function of the capillary pressure, which is in turn governed by the properties of the pore system in concrete. As water penetrates the concrete it carries any dissolved contaminants, such as chloride ions, along with it. This process can be extremely rapid with chloride contaminated water penetrating up to a depth of several centimetres in a few hours at first contact with dry concrete. The concentration of chlorides from the drying cycle can substantially increase surface concentrations and chloride ingress.

The net movement of chloride ions does not always occur away from the external surface into the concrete. Chloride ions may leach out from the concrete when the external surface is in contact with water that has a lower chloride concentration than that of the pore solution near the surface. This can occur when the surface is wetted by rain.

The movement of chlorides within concrete is further complicated by the physical and chemical interactions that take place between the chloride ions and the cement matrix.

This process, known as chloride binding, effectively removes chlorides from the pore solution and retards the rate of chloride ingress into concrete. The level of binding is concentration dependent with a greater percentage of free chlorides at higher chloride levels. Chloride binding is influenced by many factors including the total chloride content, the pore solution pH, the phase composition of cement and temperature. Glass *et al* (1997) presented a comprehensive review of the various factors affecting chloride binding. Importantly the development of carbonation in the surface of the concrete unbinds chlorides releasing them into the pore solution. When examining chloride profiles in the surface layers of concrete they should be related to the location of the carbonation front.

4.3.4 Carbonation of concrete

The hydration of cement produces solid calcium silicate hydrate, calcium hydroxide and an alkaline solution in the pores of concrete. When carbon dioxide diffuses into concrete from the atmosphere, it combines with water to form carbonic acid, which reacts with the calcium hydroxide and alkaline pore solution to produce carbonates. Similarly carbonic acid in ponded rainwater can contribute to the process. This process is known as carbonation. Carbonation may be represented by the reaction of calcium hydroxide and carbon dioxide as follows:

$$Ca(OH)_2 + CO_2 \rightarrow CaCO_3 + H_2O$$

This reaction results in a drastic reduction in the pH of the pore solution from around 13 to about 8. Once the carbonation front reaches the depth of the reinforcement the passivating film on the surface of the steel is no longer stable in the low pH environment and breaks down. Carbonation can result in the depassivation of the steel surface over a substantial region giving rise to general corrosion with many active sites acting as anodes.

The depth of carbonation depends on the rate of carbon dioxide penetration into concrete. CO_2 diffuses into concrete as a gas, moving through the dry interconnected pore structure of unsaturated concrete. The driving force is the partial pressure of carbon dioxide in the atmosphere, which under normal exposure conditions is assumed constant. The rate of diffusion of CO_2 is a function of the concrete water-binder ratio, compaction, curing, mix composition and the internal moisture content distribution. As is the case with chloride ion diffusion, concretes with high water-binder ratio are more porous and have a more interconnected pore structure resulting in substantially higher diffusion rates for CO_2 than concretes with low water-binder ratios. At the same water-binder ratio, carbonation depths are greater for blended cement concretes than for OPC concretes.

Quantifying this phenomenon is further complicated by the effect that the carbonation reaction itself has on the transport properties of concrete, which are as a result of induced volumetric and pore structure changes. In the case of blended cements, such as those containing blast furnace slag or pfa, carbonation may lead to an increase in the permeability of the concrete, and so a corresponding increase in the rate of CO_2 penetration. An opposite effect has been observed in the case of OPCs where carbonation leads to a decrease in permeability. Improper compaction and inadequate surface hydration due to lack of wet curing can also dramatically reduce the carbonation resistance of concrete.

The critical factor controlling the rate of carbonation in concrete is the moisture content distribution. CO_2 diffuses through concrete as a gas and the solubility of CO_2 in water is very low, so if concrete is saturated, the diffusion of CO_2 is extremely restricted. CO_2 will penetrate most rapidly in dry concrete, but the absence of water limits the chemical reaction between the CO_2 and concrete. So the critical internal moisture condition for carbonation occurs at intermediate moisture levels where the moisture content is sufficiently low to allow CO_2 gas to readily penetrate the concrete but at the same time sufficient water is available for the chemical reaction to proceed. An internal relative humidity of approximately 50 to 70 per cent is ideal. As with most chemical reactions, an increase in temperature results in an increase in the carbonation rate.

When predicting or measuring carbonation rates in concrete the moisture state of the concrete on each face needs to be considered. An external column or beam face sheltered from rain will have a greater depth of carbonation than the rain wetted outer face.

4.3.5 Service life models limited for use with automated monitoring

The chloride ingress and carbonation models reviewed with limited potential for use in combination with automated monitoring are summarised in Table 4.3 and discussed below. For a detailed description of these models refer to Sections 2.3 and 2.4 of DTI Report 2.

Table 4.3 *Chloride ingress and carbonation models*

	Analytical models	Numerical models		
Chloride ingress	DuraCrete (2000)	Life-365 (Thomas and Bentz, 2000)	ClinConc (Tang, 1996)	HETEK (Nilsson *et al*, 1997)
Carbonation	DuraCrete (2000)	Saetta *et al* (1993)	Isgor and Razaqpur (2004)	Khunthongkeaw and Tangtermsirikul (2005)

Note
Shading: potential for use with automated monitoring (dark grey), limited input from automated monitoring (light grey), not suitable for use with automated monitoring (no shading)

Analytical models:

The analytical model presented for chloride ingress in DuraCrete is based on the well known closed-form solution to Fick's second law of diffusion (Equation 4.2). Diffusion is considered to be the sole transport mechanism. The solution is derived assuming a constant chloride concentration at the concrete surface and a time-invariant rate of chloride diffusion. Various correction factors are specified to account for the concrete properties (water-binder ratio, cement type), curing method, environmental conditions (submerged, tidal zone, splash zone, atmospheric) and the age of the structure.

The DuraCrete model for carbonation assumes the depth of carbonation increases with the square root of time, as in most analytical models. Similar to the chloride ingress model, the input variables are determined on the basis of compliance tests, cement type (OPC with or without GGBS), curing regime, age of the structure and the external environmental conditions.

The DuraCrete models are typical of other analytical models found in the literature. All the input parameters are specified based on the analysis of data obtained from laboratory tests and field exposure trials. The models provide no meaningful way in which intelligent monitoring techniques can be applied.

Numerical models:

For the chloride ingress models Life-365 and ClinConc, the use of intelligent monitoring is primarily limited to measuring variations in the temperature profile within concrete, which can be used to modify the chloride diffusion coefficient D as a function of space and time in the analysis. The HETEK model, which attempts to model the effects of both chloride ion diffusion and convection, predicts the moisture content distribution in the concrete as an intermediate step. Direct monitoring of moisture content profiles, as described in Section 3.6, and their input into a modified form of the HETEK model, would simplify the approach and would improve the accuracy of predictions. However, numerical models such as these typically require more than 10 other inputs that cannot be determined by monitoring and so current numerical models of chloride penetration are not appropriate for use with monitoring.

The carbonation models predict the time-variant moisture distribution and the temperature profile within concrete by jointly solving the coupled differential equations. The diffusion of carbon dioxide and the rate of chemical reaction are then predicted as a function of the internal concrete environment. The resulting numerical models require a significant number of input parameters, very few of which may be determined by monitoring.

However the complexity of the numerical models could be considerably simplified if the numerical prediction of the moisture and thermal gradients within concrete were omitted from the analysis and instead were obtained directly by automated monitoring. Sensors can be installed in concrete to measure the relative humidity and temperature at given locations with time (Sections 3.5 and 3.6). The information gathered from the sensors describing the internal concrete environment could then be used as input data for the numerical models so that carbonation could be predicted as a function of the actual distribution of temperature and moisture content in concrete. Not only would this improve the accuracy of the predictions, but it would also greatly reduce the number of input parameters required for the analysis.

4.3.6 Service life models most suited for use with automated monitoring

4.3.6.1 Corrosion front prediction

A direct and simple approach to estimating the time to corrosion initiation is to monitor the rate at which the *corrosion front* penetrates into the concrete (Section 3.4.4). This involves installing an array of monitored half cell sensors adjacent and connected to shallow reinforcement at a range of depths. These will pick up the initiation of corrosion as chlorides penetrate. These data combined with data on the profile of penetrating chlorides and carbonation can be used in predictive modelling and possibly for planning a timely intervention before corrosion causes damage.

There is a monitoring technique using an anode-ladder system fitted at the time of construction (Raupach and Schiessl, 2001). This is a macrocell sensor system consisting of anodes (black steel) and a cathode (noble metal). In chloride-free and uncarbonated concrete these electrodes are protected against corrosion by the high alkalinity of the concrete pore solution. In such conditions the flow of electrical current between the electrodes is negligibly low. However when the chloride threshold level is exceeded or there is a drop in pH due to carbonation, the passivating layer on the surface of the anode breaks down. As the cathode is constructed from a noble metal it is corrosion resistant and is not affected by the change in its surrounding conditions. In the presence of sufficient moisture and oxygen, oxygen reduction takes place at the cathode resulting in a flow of electrons between the corroding anode and the cathode.

This flow of current can be easily measured. In theory, by placing anodes at varying depths within the concrete cover and measuring the electrical currents and voltages between the electrodes at regular intervals, the corrosion state of each anode can be monitored with time. However, after over 15 years, with more than 800 installed in bridges, tunnels and foundations, there is little evidence that corrosion has been detected on any of the structures where these cells have been installed. There are also practical difficulties in placing the gauges where the most severe conditions will arise and in compacting the concrete round the congested bars so that the concrete is representative of that in other areas.

The anode-ladder system is illustrated in Figure 4.1. Service life models used in combination with these monitoring techniques are mathematically very simple. By observing the time to corrosion of each anode located at a specified depth, simple regression analysis can be used to obtain a mathematical expression describing the rate of penetration of the corrosion front. By extrapolating this relationship to the depth of the actual reinforcement, the duration of the initiation phase can be estimated as shown schematically in Figure 4.1. It is worth noting that, in the case of chloride-induced reinforcement corrosion, knowledge of the chloride threshold level is not required to predict the duration of the initiation period. However the inherent variability of concrete and exposure conditions will necessitate data from a range of locations to be analysed to establish a realistic model.

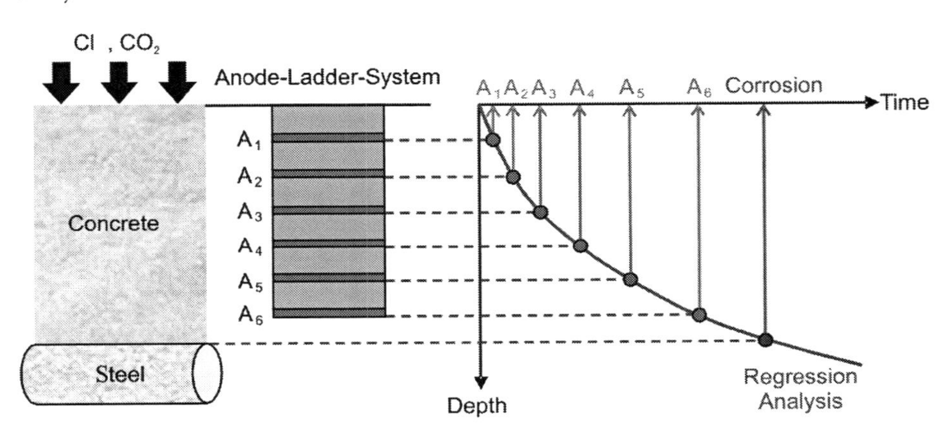

Figure 4.1 *Anode-ladder system to detect corrosion front penetration*

On many structures the early stages of corrosion will be evident from inspection and half cell surveys. Data from these surveys (which also provide a measure of variability) related to the cover depth, exposure condition, degree of corrosion and chloride and carbonation profiles, can be used to back analyse to the initiation time and to predict likely future trends.

4.3.6.2 *Direct monitoring of contaminants*

Several sensors are now under development to measure the concentration of chloride ions in concrete (Section 3.7.2). By embedding such sensors at varying depths in the concrete cover without disturbing the surrounding concrete properties, it should, in theory, be possible to directly monitor the ingress of chloride ions into concrete. Such real time monitoring data could be used to predict the time to the onset of reinforcement corrosion although it should be recognised that this method involves estimating the chloride threshold level at which corrosion starts.

Unfortunately the potential of these techniques is severely limited due to the deficiencies in the sensor technologies now available (Section 3.7.2).

Once suitable sensors have been developed, two different methodologies can be envisaged to predict the time to corrosion based on the observed spatial and temporal variations of the chloride concentration profile. The first involves estimating the rate of penetration of chloride ions into concrete through regression analysis of the measured chloride concentration profiles at regularly spaced time intervals. In this manner the evolution of the chloride concentration profile as a function of time can be predicted and the onset of reinforcement corrosion identified when a specified chloride threshold level is exceeded at the depth of the reinforcement. The second methodology is concerned with detecting the times at which a specified chloride threshold level is exceeded at varying depths from the exposed surface. Through regression analysis of the collated data, the rate of penetration of the chloride corrosion front can be determined and used to predict the time taken for the chloride threshold level to reach the depth of the reinforcement.

Several sensors are also now under development to measure the pH of pore solution in concrete (Section 3.7.3). In theory, the time to the onset of carbonation induced corrosion can be estimated by embedding sensors at varying depths within the concrete cover to detect the sudden drop in the pH of the pore solution as the carbonation front penetrates into the concrete. Regression analysis of the collated data should allow the rate of penetration of the carbonation front to be determined and the time taken for it to reach the reinforcement depth predicted. Unfortunately, as with chloride monitoring, the potential of these techniques is severely limited due to the deficiencies in the sensor technology now available. The performance of the sensors developed so far in terms of accuracy, reliability and endurance is questionable and they are not yet suited for monitoring of structures.

The lack of a sensor to reliably monitor carbonation depth is not a real problem in most practical situations for many reasons. First, carbonation-induced corrosion is rarely expected to occur in new structures because the use of an appropriate concrete together with good workmanship and control of reinforcement cover will usually result in the carbonation depth not reaching the depth of the reinforcement within the service life required for most structures. The only new structures that might be expected to be at risk from carbonation-induced corrosion are those with exceptionally long design lives or in unusually high CO_2 industrial environments. Second, carbonation depth is easily measured with a pH indicator spray applied to a freshly broken surface of concrete and while this is destructive, for most structures it is easily implemented. This is in contrast to chloride-induced corrosion where even very well specified and constructed structures are at risk and where multiple samples should be tested in a lab to determine chloride profiles.

4.4 REINFORCING STEEL CORROSION PROPAGATION

4.4.1 Introduction

The service life of reinforced concrete structures at risk of reinforcement corrosion can be defined in terms of the duration of the corrosion initiation period. However this may be regarded as an over-conservative failure criterion because the end of the initiation phase only signifies the onset of reinforcement corrosion and the structure is yet to suffer any adverse affects that may inhibit its functional performance. Several other possible limit states that occur during the propagation phase of reinforcement corrosion may be used to define a more suitable failure criterion to signify the end of the structural service life, as shown in Figure 4.2.

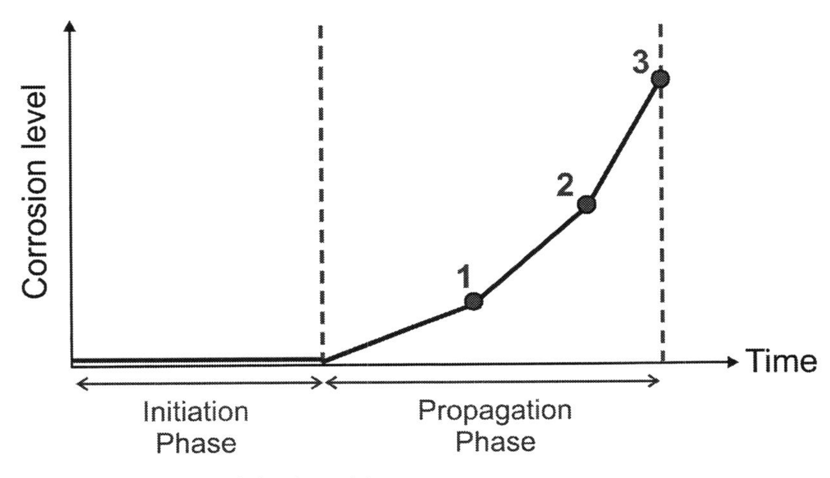

Figure 4.2 *Possible limit states for service life definition*

Each limit state is briefly discussed below:

Limit state (1) – Cracking of the concrete cover:

The onset of reinforcement corrosion produces rust, which is deposited in the vicinity of the corroded steel. Initially the corrosion products dissipate into the surrounding pore space. However, the volume of rust is significantly greater than the volume of the steel it displaces and so the corrosion products then apply an internal pressure on the surrounding confining concrete. The resulting internal pressure induces expansive stresses in the concrete cover that cracks when the applied tensile stresses exceed the tensile strength of concrete. Corrosion induced cracking of the concrete cover may be a more appropriate failure criterion by which to define the design service life as it provides an early warning of the continuing corrosion of reinforcement before any detrimental loss of structural performance. The reduction in the steel cross-section associated with first cracking of the cover is no more than 0.5 mm (Vu *et al*, 2005). This is too small to have a significant effect on the steel-concrete bond or the load-bearing capacity of an element. Also the presence of cracks helps the ingress of deleterious species into concrete and may lead to an increased rate of reinforcement corrosion. The cracking of concrete as a consequence of reinforcement corrosion is considered a serviceability limit state.

Limit state (2) – Spalling of the concrete cover:

If the corrosion of reinforcement continues unabated, the continuing expansion of the corrosion products will result in the formation of longitudinal cracks in concrete parallel to the main reinforcement. Eventually this will lead to the spalling and delamination of the concrete cover. At this stage there may be a corresponding reduction in the bond between the reinforcement and concrete due to a loss of bar confinement provided by the concrete cover and significant changes in the boundary conditions at the steel-concrete interface. The loss of bond has an adverse effect on both the serviceability and ultimate load-capacity of a reinforced concrete member. The loss of serviceability may occur as a result of excessive deflections while the load-capacity will be altered due to a lack of strain compatibility between the reinforcement and concrete resulting in the redistribution of stresses within the member. The geometrical characteristics of the delaminated zone are a function of the location and spacing of the reinforcement, the depth of concrete cover and the tensile strength of concrete. The spalling of the concrete cover is generally considered as a serviceability limit state. However if its occurrence endangers human life, for example falling concrete from a bridge onto the roadway below, then it should be considered as an ultimate limit state.

Limit state (3) – Structural collapse:

Further corrosion of the reinforcement will result in substantial loss of the steel cross-sectional area and the total loss of bond strength between the steel and concrete. This will have a detrimental effect on the load-bearing capacity and ductility of the reinforced concrete member eventually leading to structural collapse. Clearly this is an ultimate limit state.

The end of the service life may be defined as the occurrence of any of the above three limit states. So to plan efficient and cost-effective repair and maintenance strategies it is necessary that the time taken to reach any of the given limit states can be accurately predicted. This requires the use of reliable and accurate mathematical models to describe the behaviour of reinforced concrete members subject to reinforcement corrosion.

Numerous publications acknowledge that the spalling of the concrete cover is a critical limit state that should be considered when assessing the durability performance of a reinforced concrete element over its intended design life. Nevertheless, a rigorous mathematical treatment to predict the time to spalling has not been presented so far. Research has been primarily directed at formulating models to estimate the time to initial cracking of the concrete cover, with spalling relegated to just an afterthought. Clearly this is a key area of interest in need of further investigation.

In the following sections models developed to predict the structural performance of corroding reinforced concrete members are presented. Three distinct stages in the degradation process are considered:

1. The time to initial corrosion-induced cracking of the concrete cover.
2. The reduction of bond strength between the steel and concrete.
3. The resulting loss of serviceability and load capacity of corrosion damaged members.

Each stage is discussed in detail following a consideration of the rate of reinforcement corrosion, which is a critical factor controlling the extent of structural damage incurred.

A phenomenon that is often overlooked is the degradation in the mechanical properties of reinforcement as a result of localised pitting corrosion. Unlike general uniform corrosion, severe localized loss of steel section is known to have an adverse effect on the properties of reinforcement, in particular its ductility (Cairns *et al*, 2005). This loss of performance should be accounted for when assessing the structural integrity of corroded members. Once the residual ductility of the corroded reinforcement falls below the minimum acceptable limit due care and attention should be taken when applying conventional methods of analysis, such as the redistribution of moments resulting from plastic behaviour, in the assessment process. No reliable models are available now to predict the reduction in the mechanical properties of steel as a function of the loss of cross-sectional area due to corrosion.

4.4.2 Rate of reinforcement corrosion

The rate of reinforcement corrosion may be expressed in terms of the rate of metal loss (g/cm²year), rate of section loss (μm/year) or current density (μA/cm²) with the latter two being the most commonly encountered definitions in practice. A corrosion current density of 1 μA/cm² is approximately equivalent to a rate of section loss of 11.6 μm/year.

The most reliable techniques for monitoring the rate of corrosion are based on measuring electrochemical changes in the steel. Section 3.4 reviews the methods available for monitoring rebar corrosion in concrete.

Based on past experience obtained from assessing real structures and by analysing data gathered from laboratory experiments, CONTECVET (2001) specifies the expected level of corrosion activity as a function of the measured corrosion current density i_{corr} as detailed in Table 4.4.

Table 4.4 *Corrosion current i_{corr} and associated level of corrosion activity*

Corrosion current i_{corr} (μA/cm²)	Corrosion level
< 0.1	Negligible
0.1 - 0.5	Low
0.5 - 1	Moderate
> 1	High

The current density i_{corr} will vary as a function of the environmental conditions. So it is recommended that to obtain a representative estimate of the actual rate of corrosion, measurements are taken at different times throughout the year to account for variations in exposure conditions.

For structural assessment purposes, CONTECVET relates the corrosion current density i_{corr} to the loss of cross-sectional area of the reinforcement. Two different scenarios are considered (Figure 4.3):

1 Generalised uniform corrosion over the surface area of the reinforcement.

2 Localised pitting corrosion.

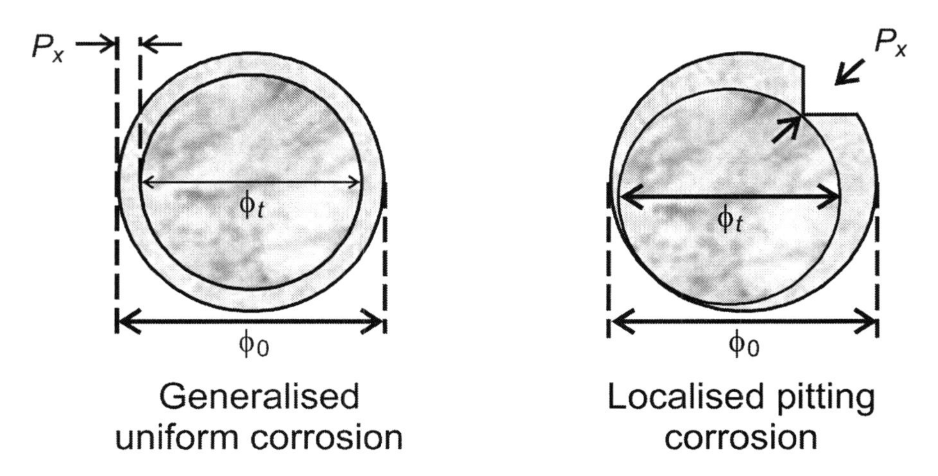

Figure 4.3 *General and localised reinforcement corrosion*

The attack penetration depth P_x is estimated from:

$$P_x = 0.0115 i_{corr} t_p \tag{4.3}$$

where i_{corr} is the corrosion current density (μA/cm²) and t_p is the time in years following the onset of corrosion. The residual cross-sectional diameter of the bar ϕ_t is determined from the following expression:

$$\phi_t = \phi_0 - \alpha P_x \tag{4.4}$$

where ϕ_0 is the original bar diameter and α is an empirical coefficient that depends on the type of attack. In the case of uniform corrosion, α is specified as 2. For localised pitting corrosion α may reach values up to 10. These recommended values for α are based upon the corrosion of a single reinforcement bar. When the loss of cross-sectional area of more than two reinforcement bars is being considered at the same location in a beam or column, it is permissible to use lower values of α in the determination of structural capacity.

4.4.3 Cover cracking and loss of bond models

The service life models reviewed for predicting the time to cover cracking and the reduction in bond strength at the steel-concrete interface are listed in Table 4.5. The potential of each model to be used in combination with intelligent monitoring is also indicated. These models are described in detail in Sections 3.3 and 3.4 of DTI Report 2.

Table 4.5 *Cracking and loss of bond models*

	Empirical models	Analytical and numerical models
Cover cracking	Vu *et al* (2005) DuraCrete (2000)	Liu & Weyers (1998) Li *et al* (2005) Pantazopoulou & Papoulia (2001) Bhargava *et al* (2003)
Loss of bond	Stanish *et al* (1999) Cabrera & Ghoddoussi (1992) CONTECVET (2001)	Wang & Liu (2004)

Note
Shading: limited input from automated monitoring (light grey)

The use of automated monitoring in all the models is limited to measuring the rate of reinforcement corrosion i_{corr}. Important aspects pertaining to the cracking and bond strength models are discussed below.

4.4.3.1 Cracking

Several empirical and mathematical models developed to predict the rate of crack propagation in corroding reinforced concrete are available. The empirical models (Vu *et al*, 2005 and DuraCrete, 2000) are computationally simple and easy to apply, as described in Section 3.3.1 of DTI Report 2. However the model parameters are obtained from regression analysis of laboratory test data, which are highly influenced by the arrangement details of the experimental programs used to collate the data. So the general application of the models in real life conditions where many parameters are different is questionable.

The analytical and numerical models considered are generally more applicable as they attempt to describe the mechanical process of crack propagation mathematically. Almost all follow the basic problem formulation as postulated by Liu and Weyers (1998), as described in Section 3.3.2 of DTI Report 2. So, initially, the various stages in the cracking of the concrete cover due to the expansion of the corrosion products as assumed by Liu and Weyers are described and the methodology adopted to analyse the problem is outlined.

A schematic representation of the idealised behaviour of the concrete cover subject to corrosion induced cracking is shown in Figure 4.4.

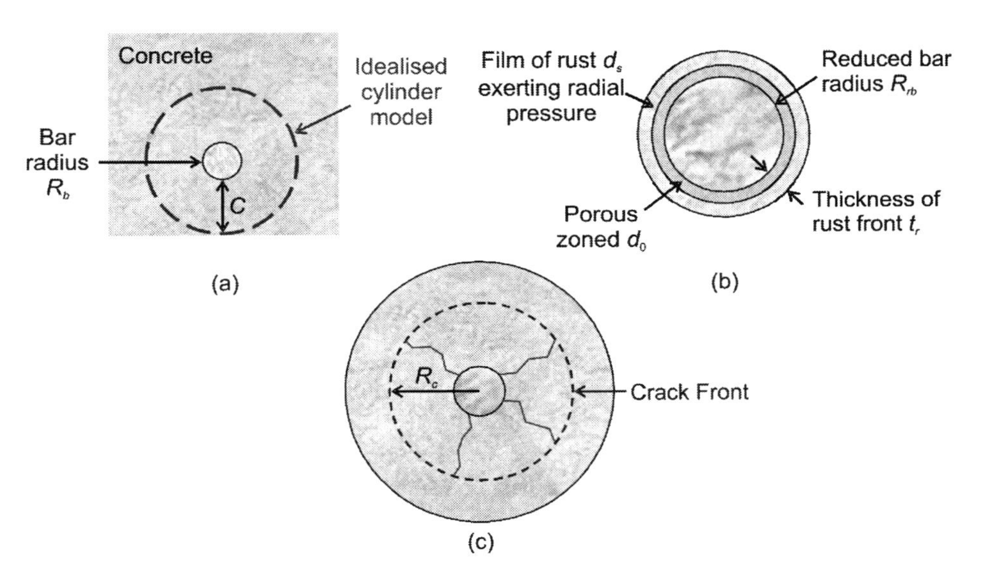

Figure 4.4 ***Idealised behaviour of concrete cover as a thick walled cylinder***

Figure 4.4a represents the concrete cover surrounding the steel as a thick walled hollow cylinder. The concrete cylinder has an inner radius R_b, which is also the original radius of the reinforcement, and an outer radius $(C+R_b)$, where C is the cover depth. It is assumed that the corrosion products are deposited uniformly around the steel surface. The cracking of the concrete cover is considered to be a three stage process.

Stage (1) – Free expansion:

It is assumed that there is a porous zone around the steel-concrete surface resulting from the transition of cement paste to steel and the presence of entrapped air voids. The volume of this porous zone is a function of the surface area of the reinforcement, water-cement ratio, aggregate size, degree of hydration and degree of compaction. Once corrosion is initiated the corrosion products will gradually begin to fill the porous zone and at this stage the surrounding concrete is not subjected to any expansive stresses. The thickness of this porous zone is denoted by d_0 as shown in Figure 4.4b.

Stage (2) – Crack initiation:

When the quantity of corrosion products formed exceeds the quantity required to fill the porous zone, any further expansion of the corrosion products is restrained by the surrounding concrete. At this stage an expansive radial pressure is exerted on the internal boundary of the concrete cylinder and this pressure increases with an increase in corrosion products. Cracks are initiated when the applied maximum hoop stress exceeds the tensile strength of concrete. The cracking begins at the steel-concrete interface and propagates outwards.

Stage (3) – Cover cracking:

As the internal expansive pressure continues to increase, the radial splitting cracks will propagate outwards in all directions to a distance R_c as shown in Figure 4.4c. At the perimeter of the crack front the tensile capacity of the concrete is reached. The concrete cover is assumed to be fully cracked when the radius of the crack front R_c equals the outer radius $(C+R_b)$ of the thick walled cylinder. To determine the stress distribution in the concrete resulting from the expansion of the corrosion products, the problem can be formulated in terms of a thick walled hollow cylinder subject to an internal pressure. The corresponding governing differential equations are then solved subject to prescribed boundary conditions. Such an approach was first presented by Bazant (1979).

All the mathematical models reviewed have adopted a similar approach to that outlined above. These models are described in detail in Section 3.3.2 of DTI Report 2. The principal differences between the models are in the specification of the prescribed boundary conditions and the definition of the concrete material properties. Where appropriate, smeared cracking is assumed and so the formulation is written in terms of average stresses and strains. The geometrical characteristics of cover cracking are a function of the location and spacing of the reinforcing bars, however all the models consider a single reinforcing bar in isolation. All the models assume a uniform distribution of rust around the reinforcement and uneven corrosion, such as pitting corrosion, is not considered. The models only predict the time to initial surface cracking of the cover and are not concerned with predicting the time to spalling, which is often of more practical importance. All the models consider the corrosion induced cracking of the concrete cover in isolation and are only concerned with applied stresses resulting from the expansion of corrosion products. However, in reality, the loading of a reinforced concrete element induces bond stresses between the steel and concrete, which result in the development of circumferential tensile stresses in the concrete cover between flexural cracks. So both the bond mechanism and the corrosion of reinforcement compete for the tensile strength of concrete resulting in a more rapid surface crack initiation time for a loaded corroding reinforced concrete element than in a corresponding element subjected to the same amount of corrosion, but with no applied loading. Very little data is available now to quantify the critical amount of corrosion products required to occupy the porous zone around the reinforcement, which must be initially filled up with corrosion products before any application of expansive pressure on the concrete.

In their published form, all of these models have a very limited use in combination with intelligent monitoring. The predicted time to cracking is highly dependent on material properties, such as the modulus of elasticity and tensile strength of concrete. The only input parameter that can be obtained via continuous monitoring of a deteriorating structure is the rate of reinforcement corrosion i_{corr}. The models attempt to predict the resulting strain distribution within a concrete element following the onset of reinforcement corrosion. However, strain is a parameter that can be directly measured by embedding sensors into the structure. The use of strain monitoring to predict the rate of cover cracking is discussed in Section 4.4.5.

4.4.3.2 Loss of bond

When a reinforced concrete element is loaded, the transfer of load between the reinforcement and the concrete occurs through the development of shear stresses at the steel-concrete interface. It is the presence of these stresses that prevents excessive slip between the reinforcement and concrete and ensures that the average strain in the embedded reinforcing bar is equal to that of the surrounding concrete. In the absence of sufficient bond strength, effective beam action as required by the codes of practice cannot be achieved and so the specified design equations are no longer valid. Loss of strain compatibility at the depth of the reinforcement results in a redistribution of stresses in the reinforced concrete element, which may lead to excessive service deflections and altered load capacity.

Several researchers have investigated the effects of reinforcement corrosion on bond strength experimentally (eg Al-Sulaimani *et al* (1990), Mangat and Elgarf (1999), Auyeung *et al* (2000) and Williamson and Clark (2002)), although relatively few models have been proposed to predict bond capacity as a function of the corrosion level.

Bond failure generally occurs as a result concrete splitting along the reinforcement caused by induced tensile stresses from dowel action of the flexural reinforcement and wedging action between the ribs of the deformed bar and concrete. Experimental investigations have shown that failure occurs when the bond stress at the steel-concrete interface reaches a critical value. This critical value is found to be proportional to the square root of the concrete compressive strength, which correlates well with the hypothesis that the splitting failure of concrete is a function of its tensile strength.

The available bond strength at the steel-concrete interface is affected by the corrosion of reinforcement. Corrosion-induced cracking of the cover reduces the confinement provided by the concrete to the reinforcement and this is accompanied by a corresponding reduction in the bond strength. The corrosion products also change the surface conditions at the boundary between the reinforcement and concrete, influencing the development of bond stresses.

There is an initial increase in the bond strength with increasing corrosion, due to the corrosion products increasing the roughness of the steel surface enhancing the friction between the reinforcement and the concrete, but with increasing corrosion the bond strength reduces and becomes negligible at high corrosion levels (Al-Sulaimani *et al*, 1990). The loss of bond strength occurs as a result of several factors. Severe localized corrosion deteriorates the ribs of the reinforcement causing a significant reduction in the interlocking mechanism between the concrete and the deformed bar. The frictional component of the bond mechanism is adversely affected by the formation of a less adhering interstitial layer at the steel-concrete interface due to the continuous expansion of corrosion products. The reduction of bar confinement resulting from corrosion-induced cracking of the concrete cover may also reduce the bond strength.

Three empirical models have been reported (Stanish *et al* (1999), Cabrera and Ghoddoussi (1992), CONTECVET (2001)) that express the loss of bond capacity as a function of the level of reinforcement corrosion. None of the models predict the initial increase in bond strength with the evolution of corrosion products. In theory, the level of corrosion could be estimated based on automated corrosion rate measurements.

Wang and Liu (2004) proposed a complex numerical model to predict the residual bond strength of corroding reinforced concrete elements. The bond capacity is estimated as a function of the available bar confinement pressure during the pre-cracking and post-cracking states of the concrete cover. The interface cohesion at the steel and concrete boundary is also considered. Before full cracking of the concrete cover it is assumed that the maximum bar confinement pressure of corroding reinforcement can reach the maximum bursting capacity of non-corroding reinforcement. The concrete is modelled as a partly cracked thick walled cylinder with cracks propagating outwards from the reinforcement as the circumferential hoop stresses exceed the tensile strength of concrete. Smeared cracking is assumed so the model is formulated in terms of average stresses and strains. The model predicts an initial increase in bond strength at the onset of reinforcement corrosion. The maximum bond capacity is reached at a critical corrosion level from which point onwards the bond strength decreases with increasing loss of steel. The theoretical predictions correlate reasonably well with reported experimental results. All of the equations are presented in Section 3.4.3.1 of DTI Report 2. The model is analogous to the models based on the idealisation of the concrete as a thick walled cylinder reviewed for predicting the time to corrosion induced cracking of the concrete cover and suffers from many of the same drawbacks as discussed in Section 4.4.3.1. The only input parameter that can be obtained via continuous monitoring of a deteriorating structure is the rate of reinforcement corrosion. Many input variables required concern the properties of the concrete and the reinforcing steel and would be more appropriately determined by sampling and lab testing.

Subsequent to the cracking of the cover, significant residual bond strength may still be available due to the confinement pressure provided by the presence of transverse steel reinforcement. This additional component of bond strength is considered by only one of the models reviewed (CONTECVET). It should be taken into account if reliable estimates of the bond capacity of corroding reinforced concrete members are to be obtained.

4.4.4 Structural performance

The most discernable consequence of corrosion is the loss of steel cross-sectional area. However, as discussed in the previous section, before the loss of reinforcement area reaching detrimental levels, the formation and expansion of corrosion products will have a negative affect on the development of bond stresses at the steel-concrete interface. The inability to develop the required bond strength will prevent the full transfer of load between the concrete and reinforcement and so alter the load bearing mechanism of the reinforced concrete element. This change in structural behaviour must be accounted for in the assessment process.

The design equations specified in the codes of practice are based on the assumption that perfect bond exists between the concrete and the reinforcement. This ensures that the strain in the reinforcement is identical to the strain in the adjacent concrete, a condition known as compatibility of strains. In this manner the reinforcement and concrete do not act as independent members, but instead behave as one composite element. However the reduction of bond strength following the onset of corrosion can lead to excessive slip taking place between the reinforcement and concrete resulting in a redistribution of stress within the reinforced concrete member. This invalidates the assumption of strain compatibility between the steel and concrete at the depth of the reinforcement and the design equations specified in the codes of practice are no longer applicable. This means that alternative analytical methods are required to assess the structural performance of corrosion damage to reinforced concrete members.

Some researchers have approached the problem by assuming a total loss of bond over the corroded length of the reinforcement. This establishes a rational lower limit on the structural performance of concrete elements subject to reinforcement corrosion. It can be considered as a realistic representation of the advanced stages of corrosion deterioration where the concrete cover has spalled over a significant area exposing the reinforcement and resulting in a complete loss of the steel-concrete bond.

Load tests on simply supported reinforced concrete beams where the main tensile reinforcement was exposed over varying lengths of the span by Raoof and Lin (1997) and Cairns and Zhao (1993) show that following the initial stages of bond breakdown, the ultimate failure load of the corroding member may not be significantly reduced and serviceability limit states, such as excessive deflections and crack widths, may prove to be the dominant assessment criteria. These studies are described in detail in Section 3.5.3 of DTI Report 2.

4.4.4.1 Failure limit states

Several limit states should be considered when analysing the behaviour of reinforced concrete beams subject to reinforcement corrosion. These include both serviceability (SLS) and ultimate (ULS) limit states. The most common and critical limit states are discussed below.

Serviceability limit states:

SLS (1) – Excessive deflections:

Over the exposed length of the reinforcement the tensile strain in the steel remains constant and does not decrease with decreasing applied bending moments. This results in a greater extension of the reinforcement and so a corresponding increase in beam curvature for reinforced concrete beams with exposed reinforcement as opposed to fully bonded beams.

SLS (2) – Excessive crack widths:

The widths of cracks in reinforced concrete beams are controlled through a combination of the clamping forces provided by the main tensile and shear reinforcements that traverse the crack openings. When the reinforcement is exposed the effectiveness of both of these control mechanisms is impaired. The reduction in applied clamping forces coupled with the increase in beam curvature associated with the loss of bond, results in an increase in crack widths in concrete over the exposed length of the reinforcement.

Ultimate limit states:

When the reinforcement is exposed the distribution of strains in the beam alters. This change in the load bearing mechanism of the beam may induce any one of many ultimate limit states that are not considered when analysing the behaviour of a fully bonded beam. The possible failure modes are indicated in Figure 4.5 and discussed below.

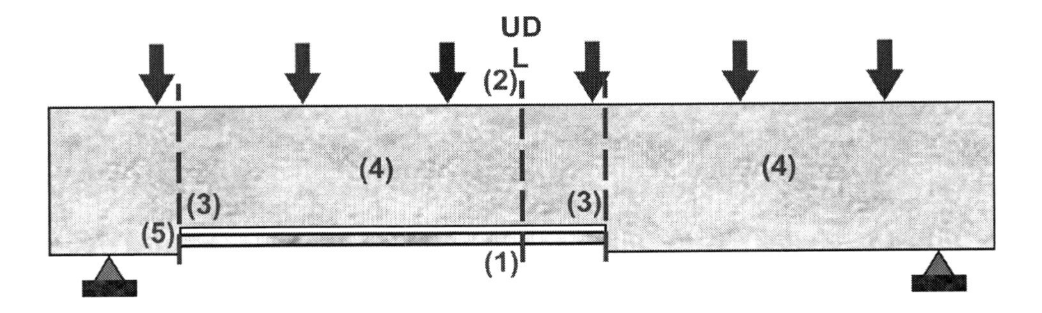

Figure 4.5 *Ultimate limit states to be considered in assessment of corroding beams*

ULS (1) – Yielding of tensile reinforcement:

Reinforced concrete beams are designed such that yielding of the tensile reinforcement occurs before the concrete reaching its ultimate compressive strain. This is to ensure that the failure mode is ductile in nature and not a sudden catastrophic compression failure of the concrete. Beams designed in this manner are said to be under-reinforced.

For small lengths of exposed reinforcement, yielding of the tensile steel is still required to produce sufficient rotation of the beam so as to allow the concrete to reach its ultimate compressive strain and so fail by crushing. For such a beam the ultimate moment of resistance is the same as that of a fully bonded beam, so the member is still referred to as under-reinforced. Once the steel yields the distribution of stress at the critical section is identical to that of an undamaged beam.

ULS (2) – Crushing of concrete at the top of the beam:

As the length of the exposed reinforcement is increased, the beam undergoes the same level of deformation as in the fully bonded case, but at a lower maximum applied strain in the tensile reinforcement. Sufficient rotation of the beam may take place before yielding of the tensile reinforcement so as to allow crushing of the concrete to occur. So failure may now take place at a lower applied moment than that of the fully bonded beam. In this instance the beam is said to be over-reinforced.

ULS (3) – Crushing of concrete at ends of the exposed reinforcement:

Over the exposed length of the reinforcement the beam behaviour changes from that of beam action to that of arch action. If the area of exposed reinforcement is of sufficient length the applied internal compression strut may induce significant compression stresses at the ends of the debonded region resulting in a crushing failure of the concrete.

ULS (4) – Shear failure:

The applied shear force in the fully bonded area of the beam is resisted by the contribution of a variety of different mechanisms. Shear is resisted through a combination of dowel action of the main tensile reinforcement, aggregate interlock, concrete in the compression zone and additional resistance provided by the shear reinforcement in the form of links or bent-up bars. However over the exposed length of reinforcement, the contribution made from dowel action of the reinforcement is lost. Thereafter due to the loss of the clamping force provided by the tensile reinforcement and the associated increase in crack widths within the debonded zone, the contribution to shear resistance from aggregate interlock is also lost. The effectiveness of the shear reinforcement in resisting the applied shear force is also impaired due to the loss in the corner anchorage of the shear links about the tensile reinforcement in areas where the reinforcement is exposed. In this region the shear force is primarily resisted by the vertical component of the internal inclined compression force resulting from arch action of the beam.

ULS (5) – Anchorage failure:

Arch action generates substantial tensile stresses in the main flexural reinforcement. The required tensile strength of the steel can only be developed if the reinforcement is adequately anchored. This imposes heavy demands on the anchorage provided and may lead to anchorage failure if the reinforcement is exposed to within a sufficiently close distance of the supports. Indeed anchorage failure accounts for the most common mode of failure for beams with un-bonded reinforcement.

4.4.4.2 Structural service life models

A brief description of structural service life models and their potential for use in combination with automated monitoring is presented in Table 4.6. Again the role of automated monitoring is limited to measuring the rate of reinforcement corrosion i_{corr}. A detailed description of each model is given in Section 3.5.4 of DTI Report 2.

Table 4.6 *Structural analysis models*

	Model description	Loading considered	Limit states	
			SLS	ULS
Eyre and Nokhasteh (1992)	Analytical Fully exposed reinforcement symmetrical about mid-span	Single-point load at mid-span UDL over whole span	-	Yielding of tensile steel Crushing of concrete.
Cairns (1995)	Analytical Half of the tensile reinforcement fully exposed	Single-point load at any location	-	Shear failure
Cairns and Zhao (1993)	Numerical Fully exposed reinforcement symmetrical about mid-span	Two-point loading symmetrical about mid-span	-	Yielding of tensile steel Crushing of concrete Shear failure Anchorage failure
El Maaddawy *et al* (2005)	Numerical Considers reduction in bond strength due to corrosion between flexural cracks	Two-point loading symmetrical about mid-span	Load-deflection behaviour	Yielding of tensile steel Crushing of concrete

Note
Shading: limited input from automated monitoring (light grey)

None of the models provide a complete description of the structural behaviour of a corroding reinforced concrete beam. Each model considers only a limited number of failure criteria with the emphasis generally placed on assessing structural performance with regards to ultimate rather than serviceability limit states. The load-deflection behaviour of a damaged beam is considered in only one model while the occurrence of excessive crack widths is not considered by any of the models reviewed. Note that in the work described it has been assumed that the reinforcement provided is continuous over the areas where the steel-concrete bond is lost. If the bond strength deteriorates in regions where the reinforcement is lapped, this may significantly impair the effectiveness of the tensile reinforcement provided and result in a substantial reduction in the load capacity of the damaged member.

4.4.5 Monitoring strain as inputs to simplified structural models

As already indicated, numerous models have been presented that attempt to predict the occurrence of undesired limit states by estimating the distribution of strains and stresses in the reinforcement and the concrete as the reinforcement corrodes with time. All the models require similar input parameters that may be sub-divided into the following three main categories:

1. Dimensional characteristics of the reinforced concrete element (eg concrete cover, bar diameter).
2. Material properties (eg concrete compressive strength, modulus of elasticity).
3. Applied loading (eg rate of reinforcement corrosion, configuration of applied structural loading).

In the last category the term *loading* is used to define all actions that induce a structural response from the element and so, in this context, it also includes the continuing corrosion of the reinforcement.

The use of these models in combination with automated monitoring is extremely limited. Many of the input parameters can only be obtained from laboratory tests or are constants relating to material properties. Site specific input data, such as the concrete compressive strength and the cover depth, only need to be quantified once by undertaking a comprehensive structural survey and do not require continuous monitoring with time. The only parameter that readily lends itself to continuing real time monitoring is the rate of reinforcement corrosion i_{corr}. A simple flow chart outlining the main steps involved in predicting the structural response of a corroding member through a combination of modelling and monitoring is shown in Figure 4.6a.

The primary objective of the available models developed is to predict the strain distribution in the reinforcement and concrete at various stages of deterioration. However strain is a parameter that can be directly monitored using the current sensor technology available (Section 3.3.2). So by embedding sensors within the concrete element, the actual strain distribution over the full depth of the element cross-section at several locations can be continuously monitored with time thereby removing the need for idealised and complicated mathematical models.

By assessing structural performance based on actual measured strain distributions in the concrete element, the accuracy of the resulting service life predictions will be improved while at the same time the computational complexity of the analysis will be reduced. This approach also enables intelligent monitoring to take a central role in the service life prediction of deteriorating structures as highlighted by the modified flowchart presented in Figure 4.6b. Four such applications of intelligent monitoring in the assessment of corroding concrete elements are discussed below.

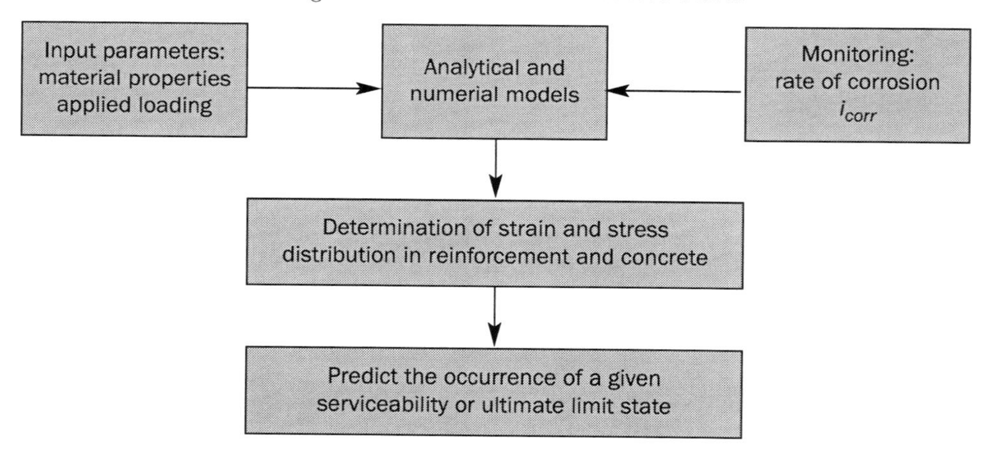

a) Proposed mathematical models used in combination with intelligent monitoring.

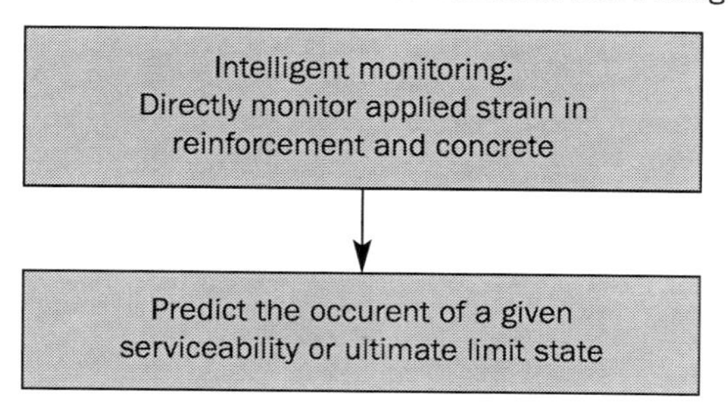

b) Modified approach to service life prediction.

Figure 4.6 ***Possible approaches to service life prediction***

Application (1) – Crack propagation:

As described in section 4.4.3.1 following the onset of reinforcement corrosion, the corrosion products formed exert an expansive radial pressure on the surrounding concrete. The resulting applied circumferential hoop strain ε_t in the concrete can be directly monitored by embedding sensors at varying depths in the concrete cover. Then it would be possible to predict the outward propagation of the crack front from the surface of the reinforcement by detecting the depth at which the tensile capacity of the concrete is exceeded.

Application (2) – Cracking of the concrete cover:

At locations where the cover is fully cracked, the concrete is unable to resist any tension and so the tensile stress in the reinforcement is at a maximum. In areas between adjacent cracks, the bond stresses acting at the steel-concrete interface transfer some of the tension force from the reinforcement into the concrete thereby reducing the applied tensile stress in the reinforcement. The location of cracks in the concrete cover can be identified by monitoring the strain fluctuations along the length of a steel reinforcement at regular intervals and detecting peaks in the strain distribution.

Application (3) – Loss of bond:

In areas where the steel-concrete bond is lost, the tensile force in the reinforcement remains at a constant magnitude. So the loss of bond can be identified by monitoring variations in the steel strain along the length of a member. Where no change in the measured strain is detected over a significant length of the reinforcement, it can be concluded that the reinforcement is either in a region of constant applied moment or there is a breakdown of the steel-concrete bond. This method may only yield reliable results where a severe reduction in bond strength has occurred.

Application (4) – Beam deflection:

The deflection of a beam can be determined using classical beam theory and the measurement of strains at multiple points along the beam. The vertical deflection v at a distance x from one end of the beam is related to the measured strain ε_x by:

$$\frac{d^2v}{dx^2} = -\frac{\varepsilon_x}{y} \tag{4.5}$$

where y is the distance from the neutral axis. From the double integration of Equation 4.5 an expression for the displacement v can be obtained. The required constants of integration and model parameters are determined from regression analysis of the measured beam strains and the application of appropriate boundary conditions. Such a methodology has been applied to predict the load-deflection behaviour of a steel bridge model (Cho *et al*, 2000). Complications may arise in distinguishing between changes in the measured beam deflection as a result of corrosion, variable loading, thermal expansion or contraction and creep or shrinkage effects in concrete.

The applications described above are most suited for use in the monitoring of newly built structures where the sensors can be installed during construction. This is particularly the case for sensors, such as fibre optics, which are required to cover a significant distance inline with the reinforcement. However the techniques described can equally be implemented for the monitoring of existing structures where it is necessary to remove areas of concrete cover, enabling the required instrumentation to be fitted, before cover renewal.

4.5 CONCRETE DETERIORATION

4.5.1 Introduction

In this section degradation processes that specifically target the concrete, rather than the steel reinforcement, are considered. The concrete may deteriorate as a result of various chemical and physical processes or a combination of both depending on the mix properties and the external exposure conditions. The most common forms of chemical attack are sulphate attack and alkali-aggregate reactions. Leaching and acid attack may also occur under less common exposure scenarios. Damage incurred from repeated freezing and thawing cycles represents the most observed and severe form of physical attack, but abrasion may also be a problem for certain types of structure.

4.5.2 Failure limit states

The physical and chemical deterioration mechanisms of alkali-aggregate reactions, sulphate attack and freeze-thaw attack vary considerably, but they are similar in that the reaction products, or ice in the case of freeze-thaw attack, expand outward applying tensile stresses on the surrounding concrete matrix that eventually degrades the concrete inhibiting its structural performance. So it seems reasonable to specify a common set of limit states to assess the long-term reliability of reinforced concrete elements with regards to these degradation processes.

Serviceability limit states:

- formation of an extensive network of internal micro-cracks. Adversely affects material properties such as porosity and permeability
- deep cracking of the concrete that helps the ingress of external deleterious species into the concrete resulting in an increased rate of deterioration
- spalling and delamination of the concrete cover
- distortion of the structure that can close joints, jam dam gates and damage adjacent structures, embedded turbines, generators, etc.

Ultimate limit states:

- degradation of mechanical properties of concrete such as loss of tensile and compressive strength and rigidity. Concrete is no longer capable of sustaining applied loading. The effects of loss of tensile strength are particularly severe when it is relied upon to carry shear, maintain bond, or contain concrete in compression.

The evaluation of the durability performance in terms of the limit states outlined above is not an easy task and there is a lack of reliable theoretical service life models available now for this purpose as will become evident in the following sections. However data from the long-term monitoring of similar structures can provide a guide.

4.5.3 Deterioration mechanisms

4.5.3.1 Alkali-aggregate reaction

Chemical reactions between alkalis from the cement (and occasionally from external sources) and minerals in the aggregate are known as alkali-aggregate reactions. The reaction leads to the formation of a gel that expands as it takes up the surrounding pore fluid. The resulting expansive pressure exerts tensile stresses within the concrete causing it to crack once its tensile strength is exceeded. Alkali-silica reaction (ASR) is the most common form of alkali-aggregate reaction and is the only kind known to occur in the UK. The reaction produces an alkali-silicate gel and it is the damage inflicted on the concrete matrix by the variable expansion of this gel that is the focus of this section.

The evolution of ASR is governed by a variety of factors including the availability of alkalis in the pore solution, the form of silica present in the aggregate particles, the internal moisture and temperature distributions and the concrete pore structure.

The moisture content of concrete is critical because the pore water acts as the transport medium for the diffusion of the hydroxyl and alkali ions required by the reaction and also the expansion of the gel is caused by absorption of water. For ASR to continue over a significant time period, it is essential that a sufficient supply of water is provided to the reaction sites. Experimental investigations and site observation have indicated that below a relative humidity of approximately 85 per cent in the capillary pores, the absorption of water into the existing ASR gel and the further formation of new gel product cease (Bazant and Steffens, 2000). However, if water later becomes available, rapid expansion and damage can occur. Sealed concrete with only mix water can become severely damaged without further water.

The reaction between alkalis and silica minerals is spatially distributed and is not uniform. The variability of the reaction and expansion due to local variations in alkali content, reactive silica type and content and moisture availability create random 3D expansions, which initiate micro- or macro-cracking in adjacent less expansive areas. This expansion process is substantially altered by the structural stress states in the concrete. Compression reduces expansion in that direction and slightly increases it transversely. Tension increases expansion and cracking. The restraint provided by reinforcement generates compressive stresses, which limit the expansion in that direction. The constraint from well anchored 3D reinforcement cages largely controls the damaging effects of AAR. With low steel areas AAR can yield the reinforcement. It is where reinforcement only constrains in one or two direction (or is absent) that serious structural problems arise (eg Exeter hospital foundations necessitating demolition).

Localised point sources of reaction give rise to the inconsistent pattern of internal cracking generally found in concrete subject to damage from alkali-silica reaction. The disruption of the concrete matrix generally produces a progressive reduction in uniaxial concrete compressive strength and a marked reduction in stiffness. Reduced Young's modulus and increased hysteresis under low load cycles is the most sensitive indicator of AAR micro-cracking and expansion to date. However it is the loss of tensile strength, which is the greatest threat to structural strength. Where tensile strength is relied on to carry shear without constraining shear reinforcement the loss of tensile strength can seriously weaken and embrittle a structure (test data, strengthening and demolition of Dutch bridges in Brabant). It also weakens the bond and anchorage of reinforcement, which is the more serious as the restraint of expansion generates extra forces in the bars. In the more advanced stages of the process, the internal cracking continues to develop eventually causing full depth cracking of the concrete cover. In the most severe cases it can result in the formation of major cracks of some millimetres in width, which extend deeply into the concrete. In time this is followed by spalling and delamination of the concrete cover. In reinforced concrete elements the cracks tend to form parallel to the reinforcement.

Overall expansion of dam structures creating damage to associated machinery, flood gates, generating equipment and most seriously the rock to concrete interface have been reported from around the world. Many of these structures are being intelligently monitored (eg Beauharnois Dam Canada). Overall expansions can also lead to problems in other large structures where there are large masses of concrete inadequately restrained by reinforcement.

For further details on the mechanism of ASR and for guidance on the appraisal of ASR damaged structures the reader is referred to the IStructE technical report Structural effects of alkali-silica reaction (1992) and the numerous publications available in specialised literature such as proceedings of the international conference on alkali-aggregate reaction in concrete ICAAR (13 conferences have been held to date).

4.5.3.2 *Sulphate attack*

The deleterious chemical reactions that take place between sulphate ions and components of the cement phase are known as sulphate attack. Sulphate attack is commonly categorised into three main forms:

1 Delayed ettringite formation.
2 The conventional form of sulphate attack.
3 The thaumasite form of sulphate attack.

Essentially the damaging effects of sulphate attack arise due to the outward expansive stresses applied on the concrete by the formation of the reaction products, principally ettringite and gypsum. The degree of expansion is a function of many factors such as the composition of the cement paste, the form of sulphate involved in the process, the source of sulphate ions (internal or external) and the concrete temperature at the location of the chemical reactions.

The induced tensile stresses associated with the volume increase of the reaction products initially result in the formation of a network of microscopic cracks in the concrete. If the process continues unabated, these cracks will grow in size over time eventually leading to full depth cracking and spalling of the concrete cover. This disruption of the cement matrix increases the porosity and permeability of the concrete and reduces its compressive strength and stiffness.

The rare thaumasite form of sulphate attack can severely compromise the integrity of the concrete by initiating the decomposition of the cement matrix, mainly the calcium silicate hydrate (C-S-H) phase, into a white incohesive mush. The outcome of such an attack is a loss of strength and total disintegration of the concrete.

4.5.3.3 *Freeze-thaw attack*

Damage caused to concrete through repeated freeze-thaw cycles is physical in nature. As the pore water in the concrete freezes it expands in volume exerting tensile stresses on the surrounding concrete. For freeze-thaw attack to be of practical concern the concrete should be saturated above a critical level. This critical degree of saturation is a function of the internal pore size distribution and structure, degree of hydration, exposure conditions, frequency of freeze-thaw cycles and the drying out of the concrete in between each cycle. Even a moderate amount of drying before the freezing of the pore water taking place significantly enhances the frost resistance of the concrete.

If sufficient empty pore space is not available to accommodate the increase in volume resulting from the formation of ice, the repeated cycles of applied stress will gradually weaken the concrete matrix resulting in a reduction in strength and the eventual disintegration of the concrete at the external surface. Non frost resistant aggregates can also absorb water during freezing cycles and expand disrupting the surrounding cement matrix. This may cause local spalling of concrete, referred to as pop-outs, above the larger sized aggregate particles.

The severity of freeze-thaw attack is also intensified by the presence of de-icing salts that alter the freezing behaviour of pore water. As the concentration of de-icing salts varies with distance from the external surface, different layers of concrete will freeze at different times, which may result in the gradual scaling of thin concrete layers. An additional affect of the application of de-icing salts is the extreme thermal gradients established between the exposed surface and the interior of the concrete. This is due to the significant drop in temperature at the concrete surface associated with the ice melting. Such thermal gradients induce substantial tensile stresses that may cause the concrete to crack.

The two classical theories of freezing and thawing of the pore water within concrete are based on the work undertaken by Powers (1945, 1949). In the theory of hydraulic pressure, the expansion of the pore water upon freezing generates a tensile stress field within the surrounding concrete matrix that results in the formation of micro-cracks when the tensile strength of concrete is exceeded. During freezing water expands in the order of nine per cent. So for the internal hydraulic pressure to develop the concrete should be saturated above a minimum level of approximately 91 per cent. In this theory the flow of pore water is away from the locations where ice is initially formed towards other regions of the concrete matrix.

However, test results have shown that water in nearby nano-sized gel pores has a tendency to be drawn to the areas where ice is being formed. This can be explained by the theory of osmotic pressure. Due to the exceptionally small scale of the gel pores, for the temperature ranges experienced during typical freeze-thaw cycles, the gel pore water remains unfrozen. The water in the capillary pores is in the form of a weak alkali or salt solution. As the temperature drops causing the capillary water to freeze, the pure water is separated from the solution resulting in increasing salt concentrations within the capillary space. The concentration gradients generated cause the diffusion of water from the gel pores into the capillary pores to dilute the higher salt concentrations. This induces an osmotic pressure differential in the direction of water flow. The diffusion process of gel pore water towards the capillary ice is further complicated by several additional factors such as localised variations in vapour pressure between the ice crystals and the super-cooled pore water and also by differential free energy levels in the ice and water as the internal concrete temperature drops.

The direction of pore water flow described in the theory of hydraulic pressure is opposite to that specified in the theory of osmotic pressure. The rate of freezing of the internal pore water determines which process is the governing mechanism. When the freezing rate is rapid, water does not have sufficient time to diffuse out of the gel pores, so hydraulic pressure dominates inducing tensile cracks in the concrete. At low freezing rates the gel water slowly diffuses into the capillary pores causing shrinkage cracks in the concrete as the cement gel contracts.

Clearly the underlying factors governing the deterioration of concrete subject to freeze-thaw attack are numerous ranging from various material properties to the prevailing external exposure conditions. Probably the most important single factor determining the freeze-thaw resistance of concrete is the distribution of the internal air-void system. Empty air voids limit the hydraulic pressure developed within the concrete and can also shorten the period of ice formation in the capillary pores. The effectiveness of the air-void system in curtailing the damage induced from freeze-thaw attack is a function of the spatial distance between adjacent air voids with a reduction in the air void spacing resulting in a corresponding increase in the freeze-thaw resistance of the concrete.

4.5.3.4 *Leaching*

The deterioration of concrete due to leaching is usually not a matter of practical concern for reinforced concrete structures in general use. However when assessing the long-term durability performance of certain structures such as dams and underground radioactive waste depositories, where the external concrete surface is in constant contact with a renewable supply of relatively pure (deionised) water, it may be of critical importance.

Deionised water contains a negligible concentration of calcium Ca^{2+} ions. When it comes into contact with concrete, concentration gradients are established between the deionised water wetting the surface and the interstitial pore solution resulting in the net outflow of Ca^{2+} ions from the concrete into the external water. This diffusion process is accompanied by a corresponding reduction in the ion concentration of the pore solution causing an imbalance in the internal equilibrium condition of concrete.

To re-establish chemical equilibrium, the loss of Ca^{2+} ions from the pore solution is compensated for by the leaching of calcium from the solid cement matrix, principally portlandite crystals $Ca(OH)_2$ and calcium silicate hydrate C-S-H. The dissolution of these minerals is driven by variations in the equilibrium concentrations. The process can be characterised in three distinct stages. Initially at high concentrations of calcium ions in the pore solution both the portlandite and calcium silicate hydrate remain stable. When the calcium ion concentration drops below a critical level, leaching of the cement paste starts with the dissolution of the portlandite. Upon exhaustion of the available portlandite the equilibrium of the system is governed by the calcium silicate hydrate, which begins to undergo partial decalcification. With further reduction in calcium concentration a second critical threshold concentration is reached at which point the calcium silicate hydrate is fully decalcified leaving behind a silica gel with no binding capacity.

Experimental studies have shown that the total quantity of calcium leached from concrete varies as a linear function of the square root of time. This implies the leaching of the cement paste is governed by a diffusion-dissolution mechanism in which the dissolution kinetics are instantaneous when considered in the time-frame describing the diffusion process.

The porosity of concrete is directly affected by the leaching process. The dissolution of portlandite in particular leads to the formation of pores on the same scale as capillary pores causing a significant increase in porosity. The decalcification of the calcium silicate hydrate does not have the same degree of impact on porosity as it results in the formation of very fine pores much smaller than the existing capillary pores.

Although the underlying kinetics of leaching are very slow, over prolonged periods leaching can severely compromise the integrity of concrete. To assess the long-term durability performance of concrete structures subject to leaching, the impact of the advance of the dissolution front into concrete on its properties should be understood.

4.5.3.5 *Acid attack*

The growth in the production of industrial and urban pollution has meant that concrete structures are increasingly susceptible to damage from acid attack. The source of various acidic species may be inorganic or organic in nature and may also be in the form of gaseous pollutants such as carbon, sulphur and nitrogen oxides.

Acid attack targets the calcium compounds in the hydrated cement paste (calcium hydroxide, calcium silicate hydrate and calcium aluminate hydrate) and reacts to form calcium salts with varying degrees of solubility. The decomposition of the cement matrix leads to a large increase in the porosity and permeability of the concrete. The rate of attack is a function of many factors such as the diffusion of the acid through the damaged concrete layer to reach the reaction front, reaction rate of the acid with the concrete, concentration and pH of the acid and the type and quantity of the hydration products taking part in the reaction. The solubility of the calcium salt formed is a key element governing the reaction rate. The less soluble the salt, the more efficient it will act in its capacity as a passivating agent retarding the reaction process. Soluble salts will readily dissolve and leach out of the concrete, contributing to its chemical deterioration. The composition and the spatial packing of the aggregate particles will also influence the severity of attack with the use of acid resistant aggregate helping to alleviate the extent of the damage incurred.

From a durability viewpoint, the consequence of acid attack is a gradual reduction in the mechanical properties of concrete. As the reaction front propagates into concrete it results in a loss of alkalinity of the pore solution, loss of mass, and a loss of strength and rigidity.

4.5.3.6 *Abrasion*

The causes of abrasion and erosion damage of concrete resulting in the progressive loss of surface material are varied, encompassing a range of contributing factors depending on the type of structure and the nature of the exposure conditions. Road pavements are susceptible to damage from the repetitive grinding action of vehicular loading and pedestrian traffic. The durability of floor slabs in industrial warehouses is increasingly compromised by the movement and storage of heavier goods and machinery.

Hydraulic structures in particular are at significant risk from long-term erosion damage. The main cause of surface deterioration is physical erosion arising from ice loading or the impact of rock and debris suspended in flowing water. In the latter case the rate of erosion is a function of the quantity, shape, size and hardness of the transported material, the velocity of flow and the mechanical properties of the concrete. An additional deterioration mechanism is *cavitation erosion,* which may occur when water moves a high velocity over a concrete surface. In this case vapour bubbles form in the water when the pressure of the liquid reduces to below its vapour pressure. The bubbles are carried downstream and collapse when entering a high pressure region. The implosion of these vapour bubbles generates impact and pressure waves that are capable of dislocating large particles from the concrete leading to local pitting of the exposed surface. So the bond strength between the cement matrix and aggregates is a critical factor governing the extent of damage incurred.

4.5.4 Service life models limited for use with automated monitoring

The service life models reviewed with limited application in combination with automated monitoring for each deterioration mechanism discussed are listed in Table 4.7. A brief overview of each model is provided below. For a detailed description of the models refer to Chapter 4 of DTI Report 2.

Table 4.7 *Concrete deterioration models*

	Empirical	Analytical	Numerical
Sulphate attack	Kurtis *et al* (2000)	Atkinson & Hearne (1990)	Marchand *et al* (2002)
			Tixier & Mobasher (2003)
Freeze-thaw attack	–	RILEM (Sarja & Vesikari, 1996)	Penttala & Al-Neshawy (2002)
ASR	–	–	–
Leaching	–	Carde *et al* (1996)	Haga *et al* (2005)
Acid attack	–	–	–
Abrasion	–	Huovinen (1993)	Horszczaruk (2004)

Note
Shading: limited input from automated monitoring (light grey), not suitable for use with automated monitoring (no shading)

Sulphate attack models:

The empirical model presented by Kurtis *et al* (2000) proposes simple arithmetic expressions to estimate the expansion of concrete under sulphate attack with time. However in the absence of any suitably defined failure criterion, it has limited use in the service life assessment of reinforced concrete structures.

The analytical model developed by Atkinson and Hearne (1990) is the most well known sulphate deterioration model and it predicts the rate of spalling of the concrete cover. Durability performance with regards to any other limit states, such as the degradation of the mechanical properties of concrete, is not considered.

Marchand *et al* (2002) formulated a numerical methodology to analyse the reorganisation of the internal microstructure of concrete subject to sulphate attack. The model predicts the evolution of reaction products and changes in the distribution and composition of the pore fluid and the solid phases of the cement matrix. However it does not directly assess the durability performance of concrete in terms of any specified limit states and so it has limited use for the evaluation of structural service lives.

The numerical model developed by Tixier and Mobasher (2003) analyses the behaviour of concrete exposed to sulphate ions in terms of the limit states as defined by the internal cracking of the concrete matrix and the subsequent reduction in its elastic properties. This is the most comprehensive model reviewed for the prediction of residual service lives. Its application in practice may prove to be problematic due to the level of sophistication in the mathematical formulation.

As highlighted in Table 4.7 three out of the four models considered provide no possibility for the use of automated monitoring in the durability assessment process, the model developed by Marchand *et al* (2002) being the exception. Even in this case the role of automated monitoring is limited to obtaining only two of the necessary input parameters, which are the internal concrete temperature (Section 3.5) and moisture distributions (Section 3.6).

Freeze-thaw attack models:

The RILEM deterioration model, the first of only two models found in researching this guide, attempts to estimate the loss of compressive strength and the rate of disintegration of the concrete surface resulting from freeze-thaw attack. However the model requires input parameters that are not readily available and it has no potential for use in combination with automated monitoring.

The second model considered is presented by Penttala and Al-Neshawy (2002) and predicts the stress state within concrete subject to applied freeze and thaw loads. The main input parameters required are the internal temperature and relative humidity distributions, which can be obtained by embedding sensors into the concrete. So there is significant scope within the proposed methodology for the application of automated monitoring. The potential of the model for service life assessment is now limited due to the lack of a suitably defined failure criterion.

Alkali-silica reaction models:

The level of complexity associated with ASR has significantly hindered the progress of research in this field. The formulation of a comprehensive mathematical model describing the kinetics of ASR in concrete is an extremely demanding task. Even when relatively simple models are developed based on idealised material behaviour (eg Bazant and Steffens, 2000) some vital input parameters cannot be readily obtained.

Several investigators (eg Ulm *et al* (2000), Farage *et al* (2004) and Fairbairn *et al* (2006)) have attempted to predict the stress state in concrete subject to ASR assuming elastic material behaviour and idealising the mechanism in terms of total stress applied on a unit volume of concrete and gel, which is composed of an effective stress acting on the solid matrix and a pore pressure in the gel. However, considering the number of unresolved issues surrounding the degradation mechanism of ASR, the reliability and accuracy of all such models are in doubt.

Leaching models:

Haga *et al* (2005) proposed a numerical model to predict the propagation of the leaching front in cement paste using a basic mass conservation formula for one-dimensional diffusion of calcium in pore water. The equilibrium condition between the solid and liquid phases, the increase in porosity due to dissolution of portlandite and the increase in effective diffusion coefficient of the cement paste due to the increase in porosity are each defined analytically by empirical equations. These equations are solved using the finite difference method to predict the spatial and temporal variations in the calcium concentration bound in the solid phase to estimate the rate of propagation of the dissolution front into concrete. More sophisticated numerical models have been formulated by several authors (eg Ulm *et al*, 1999), Mainguy and Coussy (2000) and Nguyen *et al* (2006)). However the level of complexity associated with such models renders them impractical for use in the routine assessment of structural deterioration.

The capability of these models to predict the service lives of deteriorating structures is highly questionable as none of the models directly consider a specified limit state. A possible failure criterion may be defined in terms of the maximum allowable depth of penetration of the dissolution front. However a more appropriate and practical approach would be to specify limit states in relation to the loss of mechanical properties of concrete. Carde *et al* (1996) investigated the effects of leaching on the compressive strength of small cylindrical samples of cement paste. The results show a strength loss of approximately 75 per cent when the leaching front has propagated throughout the whole volume of the sample. An analytical formula is derived to estimate the compressive strength of the sample as a function of the ratio of the degraded area. However the formula contains an empirical parameter that can only be determined through regression analysis of experimental data obtained from the compression tests. Further research work is required to reliably predict the degradation of the mechanical properties of concrete subject to long-term leaching.

None of the models reviewed are suitable for use in combination with automated monitoring.

Acid attack models:

The mathematical modelling or simulation of acid attack is a very complex process. It requires detailed knowledge of the chemical reactions taking place between the acid, the solid hydration products and the aggregate particles. The movement of all relevant ionic species within the damage zone should also be described. No viable service life models for the prediction of concrete deterioration due to acid attack were identified in the course of this investigation.

Abrasion models:

Huovinen (1993) considered the abrasion of concrete structures in arctic sea regions by moving ice sheets. The dominant factors governing the extent of abrasion damage were identified to be the temperature of the ice, the stress intensity of the ice against the concrete surface as determined from a friction test, the compressive strength of the concrete and its resistance to freeze-thaw attack. Three possible abrasion mechanisms were proposed:

1. The abrasion of the cement paste matrix.
2. The abrasion of the cement paste including the loosening of protruding aggregate particles.
3. The abrasion of cement paste following extraction of the aggregate particles.

In the latter case it is assumed that the bond strength between the cement matrix and the aggregate particles is very weak. The ice loading is idealised as a normal stress component σ and a shear stress component τ acting perpendicular and parallel to the concrete surface respectively.

Based on the results of laboratory tests and field measurements in combination with non-linear finite element analysis of the problem, an analytical model for the total abrasion depth was proposed, with input variables of concrete compressive strength, aggregate grading, the ice sheet movement, the number of ice impacts during ice sheet movements, and the number of ice impacts at which the depth of the crack generated equals the radius of the surface aggregate particles.

Horszczaruk (2004) investigated the abrasive wear of concrete in hydraulic structures resulting from the repeated impact of rubble carried by flowing water. A laboratory test method was developed for simulating the in situ conditions of concrete abrasion using an aggregate-water mixture to reproduce the environmental loading on the structure. A complex numerical model was formulated to estimate the extent of abrasion damage as a function of the work done by the abrasive mix. However this model is limited to predicting the short-term response of concrete and further work is necessary if it is to be extended to consider the effects of abrasion loading over long exposure periods.

Neither of these models is suitable for use in conjunction with automated monitoring.

4.5.5 Predictions based on expansion monitoring

In the models reviewed so far, the application of automated monitoring has found limited use in the service life assessment of reinforced concrete elements where the concrete matrix is degrading as a direct result of chemical and physical attack. The majority of input parameters required cannot be obtained through real time monitoring of structural performance. In the few cases where embedded sensor data can be used, it is restricted to measuring spatial and temporal variations in the internal concrete temperature and relative humidity distributions.

An alternative approach for evaluating the durability performance of such deteriorating structures is proposed based on the principal of a maximum allowable critical strain threshold for concrete elements. For example, such a strain threshold may be defined as a function of the loss of concrete compressive strength, extent of internal damage, loss of structural rigidity or maximum permissible crack widths. By monitoring the applied strains in concrete using embedded sensors at various depths and locations, the durability performance of a structure can be quantified in real time. The time taken for the structure to be deemed unfit for purpose may then be estimated through extrapolation of the collated data. In this manner many of the uncertainties associated with the application of the models reviewed are avoided while simultaneously the role of intelligent monitoring is significantly enhanced in the service life prediction process. The potential of this methodology in assessing the durability performance of concrete elements subject to sulphate attack, freeze-thaw attack and alkali-silica reaction is explored in the following sections.

4.5.5.1 *Alkali-silica reaction*

Carse and Dux (1990) investigated the durability performance of four high strength concrete bridge structures located in Australia subject to ASR. Mechanical strain gauges attached to the soffit of prestressed concrete bridge beams were used to measure the expansive strains resulting from ASR with time. Concurrently the associated total crack width over the length of the beams considered was also monitored. The results of the study indicate a good correlation between the observed crack widths and the reported beam expansions due to ASR.

Since then several more rigorous attempts have been made to relate the expansion of concrete undergoing ASR to the evolution of surface cracking. Fan and Hanson (1998) carried out a laboratory experiment to determine the deleterious effect of ASR expansion on the structural behaviour of reinforced concrete beams. Beam specimens 1500 mm long, 150 mm wide and 250 mm deep were cast using ordinary Portland cement and were reinforced with tension steel and shear links. Nominal compression steel was provided for the placement of the shear reinforcement. The beams were immersed in a cyclically heated alkali solution for one year to induce accelerated ASR. The expansion and surface cracking of the beams as a direct consequence of ASR were monitored throughout the duration of the test. Longitudinal cracks were first observed at the top of the beams at an expansion strain of approximately 500 micro-strain. Initially the cracks were at isolated locations. However in time the cracks grew and interconnected to form continuous cracks running along the length of the beams. Transverse cracks were also generated which gradually developed and joined the main longitudinal cracks. After one year the maximum cracks at the top of the beams were typically 0.5mm wide and the expansion was around 1500 micro-strain.

The impact of ASR expansion on the mechanical properties of concrete is considered explicitly in the IStructE technical report Structural effects of alkali-silica reaction (IStructE, 1992). Tests conducted on unrestrained concrete specimens subject to ASR show a reduction in compressive strength, tensile strength and elastic modulus as shown in Table 4.8. Under service conditions the degradation in mechanical properties is not expected to be as severe as indicated. In actual structures, concrete is generally restrained by adjacent material and by the presence of reinforcement. It also experiences a biaxial or triaxial stress state. Such effects tend to limit the degree of damage sustained by the concrete and result in an improvement in its structural performance.

Table 4.8 *Degradation in concrete mechanical properties as a function of free expansion*

Free expansion (mm/m)	0.5	1.0	2.5	5.0	10.0
	% strength compared to 28 day undamaged concrete				
Cube compression	100	85	80	75	70
Uniaxial compression	95	80	60	60	-
Tension	85	75	55	40	-
Elastic modulus	100	70	50	35	30

Fan and Hanson (1998) also considered the impact of ASR on the mechanical properties of concrete. A series of concrete cylinders were subjected to accelerated ASR and the degradation in the compressive strength, splitting tensile strength and relative dynamic modulus of elasticity were determined as a function of time and the expansive strain. The results of the investigation are presented as graphs in DTI Report 2. It was clear that the mechanical behaviour of concrete was directly influenced by the extent of ASR expansion. After a period of 180 days the loss of compressive strength, splitting tensile strength and dynamic modulus of the specimens was 24, 38 and 31 per cent respectively compared to the corresponding 28-day values.

Mohammed *et al* (2003) conducted a detailed experimental program to assess the performance of plain and reinforced concrete specimens under induced ASR. Similar relationships for the degradation of the mechanical properties as a function of the concrete tensile strain can be deduced from the data obtained in the study.

Jones and Clark (1994) formulated an analytical equation to predict ASR expansion as a function of the sum of the crack widths measured over a given length based on the results of several previous investigators.

$$\varepsilon_{exp} = \frac{\beta \Sigma w \sin(\theta)}{L} + \varepsilon_c \quad (4.6)$$

where ε_{exp} is the actual expansive strain along a reference line, L is the length of the strain reference line, w is the width of crack perpendicular to its direction, θ is the angle at which the cracks cross the strain reference line, β is a constant and ε_c is the expansive strain required in the concrete surface for initial cracking to occur. By analysing the data obtained from a large number of tests involving concrete cylinders and beams undergoing induced ASR, values of 1.5 and 2000 microstrain were specified for β and ε_c respectively. However it should be noted that obtaining reliable estimates for these parameters is a difficult task as they are strongly influenced by the size and shape of the structural member, material properties and the degree of restraint provided by the external loads and the internal reinforcement.

From the forgoing discussion it is evident that the critical strain threshold with regards to ASR can be defined as a function of either the maximum permissible crack width or the maximum acceptable level of degradation in the mechanical properties of concrete. This approach provides the possibility of employing automated monitoring in the form of strain sensors placed at critical locations thereby providing advance warning should there be a risk of the critical strain threshold being exceeded. In this way the durability performance of concrete structures at risk from ASR could be monitored.

A critical factor governing the rate of ASR and the later expansion of the alkali-silica gel formed is the availability of water. Below an upper limit of about 80 per cent relative humidity within concrete, the structural effects of ASR are insignificant. For a relative humidity level ranging between 85 to 90 per cent there is a noticeable increase in the measured expansion of the concrete. The rate of expansion is most rapid when relative humidity exceeds the 90 per cent limit.

So it is clear that the risk of damage to concrete as a consequence of ASR can be assessed by installing sensors within structures to monitor the internal relative humidity and moisture content distributions. A disadvantage of such an approach is that it is not possible to quantify the actual extent of ASR incurred damage or to estimate the reduction in the mechanical properties of concrete as can be done with the expansion monitoring technique.

4.5.5.2 *Sulphate attack*

Ouyang *et al* (1988) undertook an experimental program to investigate the impact of sulphate attack on the development of the compressive strength of Portland cement mortars. Both internal and external sulphate attack were considered and many factors such as the cement type, cement content, water-cement ratio and the addition of fly ash were included in the study. Cement hydration caused an initial gain in compressive strength with ettringite and gypsum being accommodated within the available pore space. However with time the compressive strength of each mortar specimen peaked and then reduced. Based on the experimental results a new failure criterion was defined in terms of a maximum permissible expansion limit for cement mortars subject to internal sulphate attack. The value of this critical expansion, corresponding to the peak compressive strength is estimated using an equation in which cement content is the only variable.

Similar experimental data were presented for mortars exposed to external sulphate attack. The expansion-compressive strength behaviour of mortars containing low calcium pfa was also considered for each form of sulphate attack. However in these cases no formulae were proposed for evaluating the critical expansion limits.

This investigation by Ouyang *et al* illustrates that it is possible to correlate the degradation in the mechanical properties of concrete to the degree of expansion observed as a result of sulphate attack. So in theory the durability performance of structural elements at risk from sulphate attack can be quantified by monitoring the internally applied concrete strains using embedded sensors.

4.5.5.3 *Freeze-thaw attack*

The freeze-thaw resistance of concrete specimens is frequently assessed in the laboratory in accordance with the ASTM C666 standard procedure A (ASTM, C666). In this test the concrete is subjected to 300 freeze-thaw cycles and its mechanical response is monitored throughout the duration of the test period. The degree of internal damage is quantified in terms of the corresponding decay in the relative dynamic modulus of elasticity of the concrete, determined as a function of the measured resonant frequency of the specimen. Failure is defined as a decay of more than 40 per cent before reaching the 300th freezing and thawing cycle. Cohen *et al* (1992) used this methodology to investigate the freeze-thaw resistance of two non-airentrained high strength concrete specimens. Both concretes tested failed to satisfy the required acceptance criterion. The authors report the average expansion of the specimens at the end of the 300th freeze-thaw cycle, but unfortunately not the expansions corresponding to the intervals at which the dynamic modulus of elasticity is reported. If such data were to be obtained, it may be possible to correlate the applied strain to the decay of the dynamic modulus. This allows the detrimental extent of internal damage as defined by the above failure criterion to be specified in terms of a critical strain threshold. So the freeze-thaw deterioration of a concrete element could be ascertained by monitoring the internal concrete strain distribution, and the residual service life of the structure could then be estimated by extrapolating the observed trends to predict the future concrete behaviour. Clearly the critical strain threshold will vary as a function of the concrete mix characteristics. No data is available now to assess the feasibility of the proposed approach so much research is necessary in this field.

Of course more straightforward and simple means of applying intelligent monitoring to determine the propensity of concrete to freeze-thaw attack must not be overlooked. For this degradation mechanism to be of practical concern, the internal concrete temperature must drop below 0°C and the concrete must be saturated to a minimum level of 91 per cent. If either of these criteria is not satisfied, there is no risk of damage from repeated freezing and thawing cycles. Such a scenario is an ideal situation for the deployment of intelligent monitoring as both the internal concrete temperature and moisture distributions can be monitored using embedded sensors (Sections 3.5 and 3.6).

4.5.5.4 *Restraint provided by reinforcement*

The expansion of plain concrete specimens subject to chemical and physical attack differs markedly from that of reinforced concrete specimens. Where reinforcement is provided, expansion is curtailed in the direction of restraint and may be significantly reduced from the case of unrestrained free expansion. The restraining effect induces applied tensile stresses in the reinforcement with corresponding compressive stresses in the concrete parallel to the reinforcement. The pattern of crack formation is also altered with the dominant cracks forming mainly in line with the reinforcement.

This phenomenon is highlighted with regards to ASR in the IStructE technical report Structural effects of alkali-silica reaction (IStructE, 1992). More recently Mohammed *et al* (2003) carried out a detailed experimental program to analyse the behaviour of longitudinally restrained concrete specimens under accelerated ASR. The results of the experiment show that the restraint provided by the reinforcement strongly influences the ASR induced strains measured in the concrete and steel.

Research of this nature has not been found with regards to sulphate attack and freeze-thaw attack. It is expected that the presence of reinforcement will also have a similar restraining effect on the expansion of concrete subject to either of these two degradation processes. Much further work is required if concrete expansion is to be reliably expressed in terms of the level of restraint available.

4.5.5.5 *Discussion*

Various methods to predict the service life of concrete structures subject to sulphate attack, freeze-thaw attack or alkali-silica reaction based on the specification of a maximum allowable critical strain threshold have been considered. Such an approach removes the need for complex mathematical models to describe the physical and chemical processes taking place within concrete in an attempt to evaluate the rate of structural degradation. By simplifying the analysis, the inaccuracy and uncertainty associated with idealised assumptions for the material behaviour and exposure conditions are avoided. The reliability of the service life estimate is also improved as it is determined as a function of the observed in-service performance of the structure. Embedded sensors placed at sensitive locations in the structure can monitor the applied strains in concrete and provide early warning should the required performance criteria be at risk of not being met.

However much research work is required to ascertain the feasibility of the methods described. Reliable critical strain thresholds should be specified for the relevant limit states (eg loss of compressive strength and maximum permissible surface crack widths) taking into account various influencing factors. The majority of the tests conducted on concrete specimens are now made on unloaded specimens. The interaction of strains generated due to the concrete deterioration mechanisms and those induced by externally applied loads should be considered. Also the impact of the internal restraint provided by the reinforcement on the behaviour of the concrete should not be neglected. The applied restraining force is capable of significantly reducing the expansive strains in concrete.

4.6 USE OF MONITORING DATA WITH STATISTICAL TECHNIQUES

4.6.1 Introduction

The application of probabilistic techniques is gaining increasing prominence in the service life prediction of deteriorating reinforced concrete structures. Advances made in this area have been driven by the need to develop a rational systematic approach to durability design and the demand for reliable management systems to assist with the optimal allocation of the limited resources available for the maintenance and repair of existing structures. A rigorous mathematical and probabilistic analysis of the various deterioration mechanisms affecting concrete structures has significant advantages over the empirical and deterministic methodologies traditionally employed in the design and assessment processes.

DuraCrete (2000) developed a probabilistic performance based durability design methodology. Similar in philosophy and format to the structural design codes, the durability design code uses the principle of load and resistance factor design (LRFD) where the occurrence of an undesired event is defined as a limit state with its own limit state function. By describing the various possible deterioration mechanisms using appropriate mathematical models (as presented in the earlier sections of this chapter) durability requirements can be analysed as a function of structural geometry, material properties, environmental conditions, applied loading and quality of workmanship. Partial factors of safety are applied to the load and resistance variables to ensure an acceptable level of safety is achieved with respect to the considered limit state. The specified safety factors are calibrated using probabilistic analysis to ensure that a pre-defined target reliability is attained. The uncertainty associated with a given deterioration mechanism is explicitly accounted for in the analysis by modelling the relevant input parameters as random variables.

Such a probabilistic based approach to durability design provides a direct link between the actual performance of a structure and its expected service life. This is a key aspect now lacking in the durability design of concrete structures, which is based on empirically specified design criteria such as the minimum allowable cover depth and maximum water-cement ratio.

The planning of essential inspection and maintenance strategies for deteriorating concrete structures is often made in the absence of complete and reliable information. The systematic assessment of damaged structures within a probabilistic framework provides a rational basis for arriving at such critical managerial decisions by estimating the reliability of a given structural component or system in a quantitative manner. Structures with the greatest risk of failure can be easily identified by ranking them in terms of their evaluated reliabilities and those that fail to satisfy the minimum required safety targets are in need of urgent repair. The cost-effectiveness of various maintenance strategies proposed can also be assessed by performing a risk-cost-benefit analysis.

The application of probabilistic methods in formulating durability design codes and in the planning of optimal maintenance and repair strategies for deteriorating concrete structures has received considerable attention in the research field with particular emphasis placed on the chloride-induced corrosion of reinforcement, eg Hoffman and Weyers (1996), Thoft-Christensen *et al* (1997), Enright and Frangopol (1998), Stewart and Rosowsky (1998), Vu and Stewart (2000), DuraCrete (2000) and Stewart *et al* (2003). However the reported use of automated monitoring in combination with statistical techniques is extremely limited despite the compatibility of these two disciplines.

This guide focuses on two key areas that are highly relevant within the context of intelligent monitoring.

1 The application of Bayesian statistics to update and improve the accuracy of service lifepredictions using data obtained from embedded sensors within deteriorating concrete structures.
2 Quantifying the spatial characteristic of the various deteriorating mechanisms affectingstructural performance through statistical analysis of the information gathered fromsensors embedded at regular intervals along the length, breadth and depth ofreinforced concrete elements.

Before addressing these issues, initially a brief introduction to the field of reliability theory is presented. This includes an overview of the possible sources of uncertainty in probabilistic analysis and a description of the main techniques commonly used to evaluate the reliability of a given structural element or system.

4.6.2 Sources of uncertainty

Uncertainty, to varying degrees, is an intrinsic property of any engineering system and can never be completely avoided. When designing or assessing the performance of a given structure, it is essential to identify and account for all the possible sources of uncertainty, which affect the theoretical analysis and the in-service performance of the structure.

Essentially each possible uncertainty can be classified as either an underlying inherent characteristic of the engineering system that cannot be totally removed or as a quantifiable error in the prediction of the system behaviour, which can be significantly reduced or eliminated through the acquisition of additional data and improved modelling.

Various sources of uncertainty are briefly discussed below.

Modelling uncertainty is a direct result of deficiencies in mathematical models to accurately represent the processes under consideration. The idealised representation of real life conditions introduces prediction errors.

Physical uncertainty arises due to the inherent variability of the basic variables under consideration. For example the behaviour of a structural component is governed by several factors such as the material properties, applied loading and exposure conditions all of which are random in nature and cannot be estimated with absolute certainty. The physical uncertainty associated with model parameters can be significantly reduced with increased availability of measured data however it can not be eliminated.

The reliability of statistical estimators, such as the mean and standard deviation, of a random variable is primarily a function of the quantity and quality of the available data and different data sets will yield different values of the parameters. This *statistical uncertainty* can be reduced, although not removed, by increasing the size of the data set used to determine the model parameters.

Human involvement is a major source of uncertainty in the design and construction of most engineering projects. This type of uncertainty may arise due to design errors, inadequate understanding of applied loading or response and poor construction practices. Uncertainty in human behaviour is a very difficult phenomenon to quantify analytically so its impact cannot be easily assessed.

4.6.3 Reliability theory

Reliability theory provides a rational and logical framework for the incorporation of uncertainty into deterministic analytical methods using fundamental probability concepts. It can be used to estimate the probability of occurrence of specified serviceability or ultimate limit states during the service life of a structure.

In a simple two-variable case where the limit state consists of one resistance parameter and one load parameter, the limit state function is defined as:

$$R(t) - S(t) \geq 0 \tag{4.7}$$

where $R(t)$ is the time-variant resistance of the structure and $S(t)$ is the time-variant applied loading. It should be recognised that the terms *resistance* and *load* apply to a much broader class of problems than the terms may initially imply. For example the limit state function may be used to model the penetration of chloride ions into concrete and the initiation of reinforcement corrosion. The *load* in this case is the chloride ion concentration at the surface of the reinforcement and the *resistance* is the chloride threshold level that should be exceeded in order for corrosion to start.

The reliability of the structure with regards to the limit state under consideration can be determined as a function of time by modelling the resistance and load parameters as random variables with probability density functions $f_R(r)$ and $f_S(s)$ respectively. For the two-variable case considered so far, the time-variant probability of failure can be stated as:

$$P_f = \left[\left(R(t) - S(t) \right) \leq 0 \right] \tag{4.8}$$

The time-dependent nature of the reliability problem is shown schematically in Figure 4.7. The structural resistance R generally reduces with time due to deterioration whereas the applied loading S has a tendency to increase with time. Also the degree of uncertainty associated with both variables tends to increase with time. These effects are represented in Figure 4.7 by variations in the mean values of R and S and also by changes to the shapes of the corresponding probability density functions, which become flatter and wider with time. A qualitative measure of the probability of failure P_f can be obtained by considering the area of overlap between $f_R(r)$ and $f_S(s)$. It is clear that P_f is a function of time. The service life of the structure can be estimated by reference to pre-defined target reliability as shown in Figure 4.7.

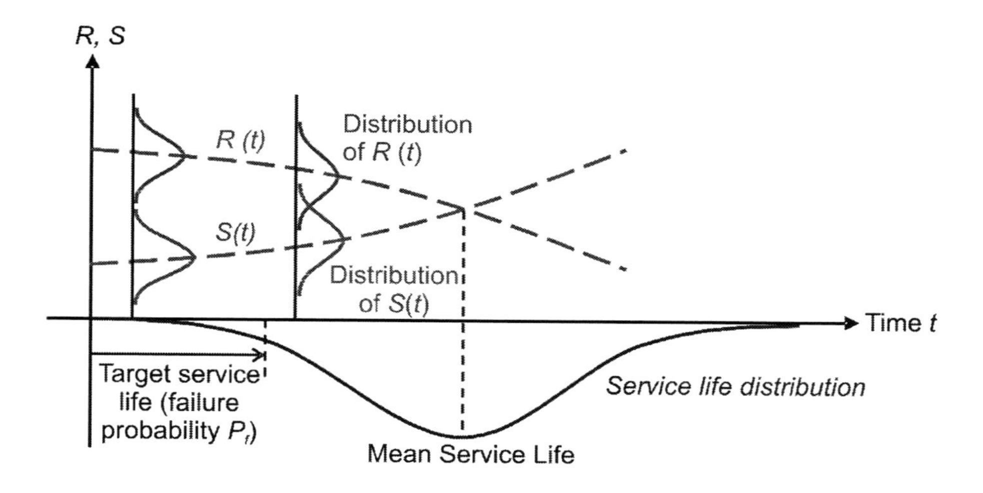

Figure 4.7 *Time-dependent reliability performance*

4.6.3.1 *Estimation of structural reliability*

To evaluate the probability of failure as defined by Equation 4.8 a knowledge of the individual distributions $f_{X_i}(x_i)$ is required. However, in practice such information is often impossible to obtain or unavailable due to a lack of data. In such cases the reliability of a given component is estimated using only the mean and variance of the random variables. In this approach reliability is specified in terms of a single parameter, the reliability index β as described in Section 5.3.1 of DTI Report 2.

Depending on the form of the limit state function under consideration, the evaluation of the exact probability of failure may be a complex task. For practical purposes, approximate numerical methods for the estimation of the failure probability have been developed. The most well known and widely used solution procedure for determining the reliability index β is the first order reliability method (FORM). An alternative to numerical methods is the application of sampling techniques such as Monte Carlo simulation.

Additionally the performance of a structure consisting of several elements is seldom assessed in terms of a single limit state. Even for the simple case of a reinforced concrete beam, the in-service operational requirements are defined as a function of several limit states such as flexural and shear failures and permissible deflection and cracking criteria (for example see Section 4.4.4.1). So to accurately estimate the reliability of a multi-component structural system, the interaction between all the relevant limit states identified should be considered. This can be achieved within the framework of systems reliability.

In essence any structural system may be idealised as either a series system or a parallel system or a combination of both depending on the complexity of the structure. In a series system the attainment of any single limit state constitutes the failure of the entire system. This type of system has no in-built redundancy and the reliability of the structure depends on the continuous safe operation of all individual components. In a parallel system the failure of the entire structure only occurs once all possible limit states have been violated. The reliability of the structure is assured if any of the individual components continue to operate safely.

An overview of the techniques described above is presented in Sections 5.3.2 and 5.3.3 of the DTI Report 2. For a detailed discussion on the theory and application of reliability theory the interested reader is referred to standard texts on the subject, eg Thoft-Christensen and Baker (1982), Ang and Tang (1984) and Melchers (1999).

4.6.3.2 *Specification of target reliability indices β*

A structure should be designed such that the probability of an unwanted event occurring during its intended service life is below a maximum acceptable risk of failure. The levels of performance required with regards to varying limit states can be specified quantitatively in terms of β. When deciding upon the target value of β, factors such as the limit state under consideration, associated repair and maintenance costs and consequences of failure should be taken into account. For ultimate limit states, where the violation of a limit state has severe implications with regards to structural performance and safety, only a very low risk of failure may be tolerated. Eurocode 1 is based on a target β of 3.8 (corresponding to a probability of failure of 7×10^{-5}) for a structure with a design service life of 50 years. For serviceability limit states, a greater risk of failure is acceptable as failure does not pose any serious safety concerns.

The total construction and operation costs over the service life of the structure should also be considered when specifying the target reliability indices. If the cost of mitigating the risk of failure at the construction phase is low compared to the cost of later repair work required should failure occur, it may be advantageous to design the structure to attain a high level of reliability to minimise any future maintenance costs. Conversely if construction costs are high compared to repair costs, it may be more desirable to design the structure to a lower level of reliability and ensure that the specified performance criteria are met over its service life by planning an effective inspection, monitoring and repair strategy.

Target reliability indices β as a function of the initial risk mitigation and future repair costs for a 50 year design service life are recommended in DuraCrete (2000) and presented in Table 4.9.

Table 4.9 *Specification of target reliability index β for a 50 year design service life*

Cost of risk mitigation relative to cost of repair	Target reliability index β
Low	3.72
Normal	2.57
High	1.28

4.6.4 Bayesian updating

Increasingly, Bayesian analysis is taking a more prominent role in the reliability assessment of concrete structures. Bayesian statistics provides a framework within which data obtained from routine site investigations and automated monitoring can be combined rationally with analytical predictions of structural performance to update initial estimates of service life. Such an approach has significant advantages over conventional probabilistic analysis where no systematic methodology is available to re-evaluate structural reliability in the light of any new information obtained regarding the in situ behaviour of the structure.

Bayesian updating will also improve the accuracy of service life predictions by reducing the uncertainty associated with the input parameters required by the predictive models. During the design phase, decisions regarding the input values of model parameters are often made based on engineering judgement and past experiences gained from constructing structures in similar environmental conditions. This introduces a degree of uncertainty into the analysis, which is reflected in the high coefficients of variation assigned to the basic random variables when assessing long-term reliability performance using probabilistic methods. The acquisition of additional data on the actual in-service characteristics of the structure such as material properties, applied loading and quality of workmanship allows the statistical estimators describing the model parameters to be recalibrated, reducing uncertainty and so improving the accuracy of the model prediction. This can be best achieved within the framework of Bayesian statistics.

Bayesian analysis is applied to estimate the future reliability of structural components based on data gathered from site inspections. Enright and Frangopol (1999) applied Bayesian techniques to investigate the influence of inspection updating on the time-variant reliability of a reinforced concrete bridge at risk of damage from chloride-induced reinforcement corrosion. Several case studies are presented in the RILEM report *Probabilistic assessment of existing structures* (Diamantidis, 2001).

These studies, along with other published work, are concerned with updating structural reliability predictions based on the results of on-site inspections carried out at certain specified time intervals. To date the use of data obtained on a more continuous basis from sensors embedded in structures has received scant attention.

In the following section a practical application of Bayesian statistics in combination with intelligent monitoring to predict structural service life is described. For an overview of the fundamental concepts of Bayesian theory refer to Section 5.4.1 of DTI Report 2.

4.6.4.1 *Application of Bayesian updating to intelligent monitoring*

The most relevant work is by Rafiq *et al* (2004a) in which a methodology is developed for utilising data obtained from sensors embedded in slabs or beams to update the predicted probabilities of chloride-induced reinforcement corrosion at the level of the rebar with time. The rate of penetration of the chloride corrosion front into concrete is monitored by a galvanic corrosion current expansion-ring-system as described in Section 3.4.4. The anodes are placed at depths of 10 mm, 20 mm and 30 mm from the concrete surface with a cover depth of 40 mm provided for the reinforcement.

The closed form solution to Fick's second law of diffusion (Equation 4.2) is used to model the penetration of the chloride front. The equation is rearranged in terms of the time to corrosion initiation T_I as follows:

$$T_I = \frac{C_d^2}{4D\left[erf^{-1}\left(1-\frac{C_{th}}{C_{s,cl}}\right)\right]^2} \qquad (4.9)$$

The parameters D, $C_{s,cl}$, C_{th} and C_d are all modelled as random variables. The required failure probabilities and the probability density function of the time to corrosion initiation are evaluated using the Monte Carlo simulation method with Latin Hypercube sampling.

Updated distributions for the time to corrosion initiation T_I are determined based on the data received from the embedded sensors. For example, in Figure 4.8 the probability density functions corresponding to various assumed corrosion detection times at a sensor depth of 10 mm are shown. The uncertainty associated with the predicted mean time to corrosion initiation reduces as more information becomes available.

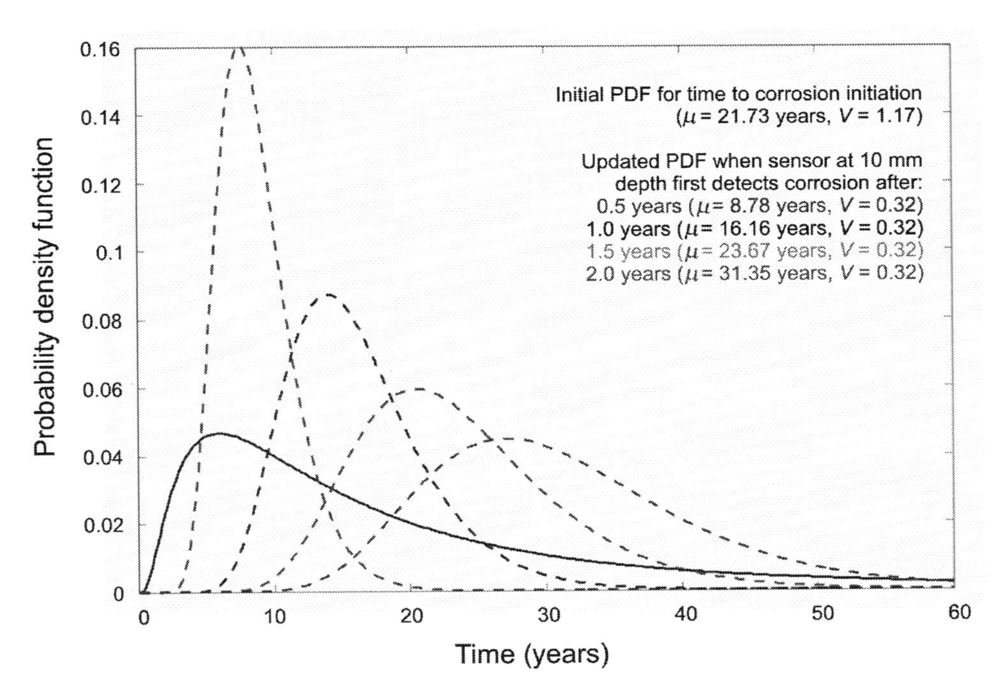

Figure 4.8 ***Updated PDFs for time to corrosion for varying sensor detection periods***

In a later study Rafiq *et al* (2004b) investigated the sensitivity of the predicted prior and posterior failure probabilities to variations in the specified probability distributions of the model input variables. The parameters considered in the sensitivity analysis are the surface chloride concentration $C_{s,cl}$, which is taken to reflect the severity of the exposure conditions, the chloride threshold level C_{th} and the cover depth C_d in combination with the diffusion coefficient D. The last two variables are considered simultaneously as both are assumed to be a function of the level of workmanship and material quality. The level of workmanship is measured by the variability in the concrete cover provided whereas the diffusion coefficient is taken as a function of material quality.

The results of the analysis show that the prior failure probabilities estimated are very sensitive to variations in the statistical estimators of the input parameters whereas the corresponding posterior failure probabilities evaluated exhibit a noticeably lower degree of sensitivity. In both cases it is found that the level of workmanship and quality of concrete have the biggest influence on the predicted reliability performancem and so improved estimates of structural service life can be obtained by reducing the uncertainty associated with the input parameters C_d and D.

The incorporation of data obtained from automated monitoring in the reliability assessment of deteriorating reinforced concrete structures can significantly improve the accuracy of service life predictions. Bayesian statistics provides the systematic and rational framework within which the new data can be combined with prior information in the durability analysis of structural components. The integration of such an assessment technique within existing management systems can greatly assist in maximising the effectiveness of the limited resources available for the maintenance and repair of damaged structures.

4.6.5 Spatial variability of deterioration mechanisms

Up to this point the uncertainty associated with the resistance and load parameters has been accounted for by modelling each relevant input parameter as a random variable with a global mean value and standard deviation. This methodology neglects the effects of spatial variability that may be exhibited by one or more of the model parameters. This in effect means that the probability of reaching a given limit state defined by the same basic variables in two different structures is the same irrespective of the size of the structures. However when considering chloride-induced reinforcement corrosion for example, the risk of corrosion in a large structure is greater than that of a small structure due to a higher probability of observing a localised peak in the chloride surface concentration or a localised drop in the depth of concrete cover provided. Clearly overlooking spatial variability may result in gross errors when estimating the probability of a given limit state being exceeded with time. In a critical review of the deterioration models now available for the prediction of service life with respect to reinforcement corrosion, Stewart *et al* (2003) identified the need for the development of probabilistic models, which include the effects of spatial variability as one of the main areas for future research.

In this section an overview of the possible sources of spatial variability is presented, followed by a brief description of the mathematical techniques used to describe the variation exhibited by model parameters in the spatial domain. The impact of accounting for the spatial variability of degradation processes on the resulting prediction of service life is illustrated by considering a simple case of a reinforced concrete beam subject to chloride attack. Finally the role of intelligent monitoring in the spatial analysis of structural deterioration is discussed.

4.6.5.1 Sources of spatial variability

Concrete is an inherently varying material exhibiting significant variation from location to location. Small scale variability arises due to the random distribution of aggregate particles, capillary pores and micro cracks within the concrete matrix. This affects properties such as compressive strength and permeability. Large scale variation occurs where there are differences in mix proportions between batches. Variability also occurs due to difficulties, or inadequacies, in construction such as poor compaction and insufficient curing. The steel reinforcement also exhibits a degree of variability in its spatial properties although due to the nature of the material this is likely to be far less than that exhibited by concrete. The concrete cover depth will generally also vary around any particular structure.

Another source of large scale variability is the spatial variation in environmental conditions over the surface area of a structure. For example exposure to rainfall, wind and external contaminants will vary from location to location. Temperature may also vary with location inducing thermal gradients within the concrete.

Material properties, structural geometry and the severity of exposure conditions dictate the service life of reinforced concrete elements. So the spatial variability associated with these governing parameters should be considered when assessing the long-term reliability performance of a given structure.

4.6.5.2 Spatial correlation structure

The spatial characteristics of the model variables may be described in a mathematical context by defining the spatial correlation function for each parameter under consideration. The correlation function $\rho(\tau)$ specifies the spatial dependence of a stochastic process X at two points separated by the interval τ. For very small intervals the correlation function is close to unity and it decays as the size of the interval increases.

The results of any spatial analysis are very sensitive to the correlation structure assumed for each of the model parameters considered in the investigation. The correlation structure is a second order characteristic of a stochastic process and is a measure of how deviations of the observed values from the mean value at different locations are correlated. Unlike other properties of a random variable that are site specific, such as the mean value, the correlation structure of a spatially heterogeneous variable is portable. Once obtained, it can be used as a reasonable first approximation to describe the spatial variation of the variable at other similar locations in the absence of site specific data.

The spatial correlation structure is discussed in more detail is Section 5.5.2 of DTI Report 2.

4.6.5.3 *Random field analysis*

A parameter that exhibits spatial variability may be described in terms of a random field by using a set of spatially correlated random variables. This is achieved by subdividing the structure under consideration into a series of elements and assigning a random variable to each element to represent the random field. The correlation coefficients between the spatially distributed random variables may then be evaluated based upon the correlation characteristics of the corresponding random field.

Several techniques are available for describing random fields in terms of discrete random variables. The most practically applicable methodology is the spatial average formulation developed by Vanmarcke (1983). By representing the random field in terms of a series of correlated spatial averages, it allows the essential features of a random phenomenon to be expressed in terms of several physically meaningful and experimentally accessible parameters such as the mean μ, variance σ^2 and the scale of fluctuation θ.

For further information on random field analysis refer to Section 5.5.3 of DTI Report 2.

4.6.5.4 *Application of spatial analysis in service life prediction*

Chloride-induced corrosion of reinforcement has been investigated within a spatial context by several researchers (Engelund and Sorensen (1998), Karimi and Ramachandran (1999), Vu and Stewart (2001), Li *et al* (2003), Karimi *et al* (2005) and Vu and Stewart (2005)). In all cases the parameters of interest are modelled as random fields as described in the previous section. The study conducted by Karimi *et al* (2005) is briefly discussed (for further details refer to Section 5.5.4 of DTI Report 2).

In this investigation the probability of the onset of corrosion initiation with time for a 5m long reinforced concrete beam is considered. The ingress of chloride ions into concrete is modelled using the well known solution to Fick's second law of diffusion (Equation 4.2). The diffusion coefficient D is represented as a spatially varying stochastic process. All other input parameters are assumed to be deterministic quantities.

A typical set of evaluated failure probabilities is presented in Figure 4.9. It is clear that the probability of the onset of corrosion with time increases with increasing spatial variation in D. Neglecting the variability exhibited by D in the spatial domain results in a significant underestimation of the failure probabilities. The results of the spatial analysis are very sensitive to the correlation structure assumed for D.

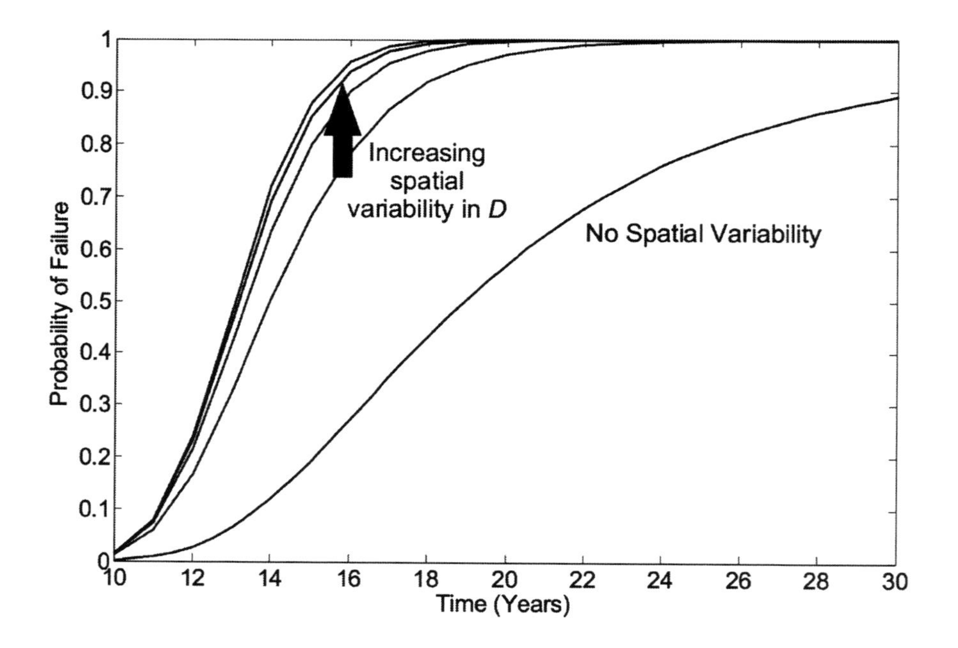

Figure 4.9 *Probability of corrosion initiation with spatial variability in D*

4.6.5.5 *Intelligent monitoring within the context of spatial analysis*

The installation of a network of embedded sensors within a structure enables continuous real time data regarding the internal concrete environment and the external exposure conditions to be collated as a function of sensor location. The availability of such data is necessary to analyse the temporal and spatial dependence of the degradation processes impairing the durability performance of reinforced concrete structures.

The critical factor governing the probabilistic analysis of a spatially varying stochastic process is the definition of its corresponding correlation function $\rho(\tau)$. An accurate estimate of the correlation function is essential if the results of the spatial analysis are to be interpreted with a reasonable degree of confidence. However there is very little data available now that captures the spatial fluctuations of the various input parameters required to model the deterioration mechanisms described in this guide so no reliable estimates of the associated correlation structures can be made. In nearly all the studies reviewed the correlation functions specified are based on a subjective appraisal of the underlying physical and chemical properties of the variables under consideration.

The one exception to this case is the probabilistic analysis of chloride-induced reinforcement corrosion undertaken by Karimi (2001) where the surface chloride concentration $C_{s,cl}$ and the apparent diffusion coefficient D_{app} are modelled as random fields. In this investigation site data obtained from three separate reinforced concrete bridge crossbeams exposed to de-icing salts are used to estimate the correlation structures of $C_{s,cl}$ and D_{app}.

To obtain reliable estimates of the correlation structure of spatially dependent variables, data sets consisting of sample measurements taken at frequent intervals are required. Automated monitoring of structures can play a key role in providing such information by embedding sensors at regular intervals along the length, breadth and depth of reinforced concrete members. The spatial analysis of the data recorded will enable the correlation structure of the parameters monitored to be determined. Once the spatial characteristics of variables such as the internal moisture content distribution are defined, it may be possible to indirectly speculate about the correlation lengths of unmonitored but related concrete properties such as the internal pore structure.

Increased knowledge of the spatial variability of the various degradation processes can also be used to provide informed guidance on the optimal placement of any future planned sensor networks. The interaction between intelligent monitoring and spatial analysis is a two-way process with each discipline yielding results that can be used to improve the effectiveness and performance of the other.

In the majority of structures monitored, sensors are placed in areas where exposure to external hazardous contaminants is expected to be a maximum and also at structurally critical locations such as expansion joints. Irrespective of the final deployment strategy, there are always practical and economical constraints on the total number of sensors that can be installed. An additional feature of spatial analysis is that observed values of a given parameter at sensor locations can be used to predict values of the parameter in areas where no sensor data is available. Statistical techniques such as kriging have been developed for this purpose and are well documented in the literature (eg Bailey and Gatrell, 1995). Again the accuracy of the analysis depends on the reliability of the correlation structures assumed in the analysis.

The time dependent nature of the sensor data gathered also allows the temporal characteristics of the estimated correlation structures to be investigated. This gives rise to the application of time dependent reliability theory, which is an important field of study in its own right.

4.7 CONCLUDING REMARKS

The vast majority of service life models presented in the literature and used by industry have been developed independently of advances made in the field of automated monitoring, so an incompatibility exists between the input parameters required by the models and what can be practically measured with installed sensors. In many cases the role of automated monitoring is restricted to providing only one or two of the input variables and in a significant number of the models reviewed automated monitoring cannot take any active role in the assessment process.

The most promising techniques are those based on directly monitoring actual physical and chemical changes within the concrete as a result of the continuing degradation process. These include methods such as corrosion front prediction and strain monitoring. Much further work is now required to verify the feasibility of these methods especially in the case of expansion monitoring with regards to alkali-aggregate reaction, sulphate attack and freeze-thaw attack.

The incorporation of sensor data within a suitable probabilistic assessment methodology can also significantly enhance the reliability of service life predictions and greatly assist with the planning of efficient and cost-effective repair and maintenance strategies.

Automated monitoring can play a key role in the service life assessment of reinforced concrete structures. A more concerted effort is required to integrate the knowledge base and capabilities of these two separate, but interrelated disciplines. There is significant scope for further research and development in this area.

5 Case studies

There are thirty two case studies concerning automated monitoring of concrete structures presented as Appendix A2 of DTI Report 1 and listed in Table 5.1 below. The case studies were selected to provide practical examples of remote monitoring using the various sensors and methods described in the main guide. They include examples measuring strain (using traditional electrical resistance strain gauges, acoustic emission and fibre optic sensors), reinforcing steel corrosion (using resistivity, potential, polarisation resistance), chlorides in concrete, moisture (using relative humidity and ETDR measurement), and soil variables such as pH, resistivity, potential and chloride. A combination of sensors is most often used because this provides a broader picture allowing more definitive conclusions to be drawn on the condition of the structure with a view to planning a maintenance schedule and estimating service life. Remote monitoring is almost always combined with periodic on-site inspection so that trends reported from the monitoring can be checked, baseline data re-established, and repairs or replacements to faulty sensors and equipment, where accessible, carried out.

Detailed information is generally lacking for most case studies reported in the literature and from equipment manufacturers for reasons of confidentiality, but sufficient information is available to provide instructive cases of the diverse approach to practical remote monitoring. The references at the end of each case study provide contacts for personal follow-up. Equipment suppliers referred to in the case studies can be located from the list of sensor and equipment manufacturers, presented in Appendix A1.2 of DTI Report 1.

Table 5.1 *List of case studies in DTI Report 1*

	No	Country	Variables monitored*
1	Austria	Schladming bridge, Schladming	Strain, temperature
2	Canada	Confederation bridge, New Brunswick	Strain, vibration, displacement, temperature, corrosion
3	Canada	Portage Creek bridge, British Columbia	Strain, vibration, temperature
4	Canada	Taylor bridge, Headingley, Manitoba	Strain, temperature
5	Canada	Toulnustouc dam, Quebec	Displacement, vibration, stress
6	China	Ting Kau bridge, Hong Kong	Strain, vibration, displacement, temperature
7	Germany	Westend bridge, Berlin	Strain, vibration, displacement, temperature
8	Netherlands/Belgium	Breda (Netherlands) and Kortrijk (Belgium) bridges	Strain, stress
9	Norway/Sweden	Svinesund bridge, Norway/Sweden	Strain, vibration, temperature
10	Sweden	Arsta bridge, Stockholm	Strain, vibration, temperature

11	Switzerland	Versoix bridge, Geneva	Strain, stress, temperature
12	UK	Kingston bridge, Glasgow	Strain, displacement, temperature, relative humidity, weather
13	UK	Catthorpe bridge, Rugby	Strain, displacement, temperature
14	UK	Huntingdon bridge, Huntingdon	Strain, displacement, temperature, relative humidity
15	USA	Boston Red Line tunnel, Boston	Strain, displacement, temperature
16	Canada	Vachon bridge, Quebec	Reinforcement potential, corrosion rate, concrete resistivity, strain, temperature, relative humidity
17	Denmark	Copenhagen metro	Reinforcement corrosion rate/probability, potential, temperature
18	Denmark	Great Belt Link and Oresund Link bridges and tunnel	Reinforcement corrosion rate/ probability, concrete temperature
19	Italy	Milan metro	Concrete potential, resistivity
20	Portugal	Docks in shipyard, Setubal	Reinforcement corrosion rate, potential, concrete resistivity, temperature
21	UK	Jubilee Extension Line underground railway, London	Reinforcement corrosion rate, temperature, relative humidity
22	UK	Limehouse Link road tunnel, London	Reinforcement corrosion rate, concrete resistivity
23	UK	Wolvercote viaduct, Oxford	Reinforcement potential, corrosion rate, concrete resistivity
24	Canada	Bridge, Ontario	Reinforcement potential, concrete relative humidity, strain, temperature
25	Switzerland	Luzzone Dam	Temperature
26	Sweden	Hylte Dam	Temperature, water seepage rate
27	Netherlands	Roadway Bridges	Moisture, temperature, displacement
28	USA	Bridges, Missouri	Concrete chloride, potential
29	China	Underground station, Hong Kong	Displacement
30	France	Tunnel, Toulon	Displacement
31	USA	Kealakaha bridge, Hawaii	Seismic event (vibration), displacement, strain

* Some or all of the listed variables are described in the particular case study, depending on the information source.

6 Looking to the future

6.1 DRIVERS FOR MORE WIDESPREAD MONITORING

At present intelligent monitoring is not widely used. The main barriers to its more widespread use may be summarised as follows.

A case needs to be made that the benefits outweigh the:

- upfront cost
- implications of involving another party
- long-term commitment.

Technical:

- some important parameters cannot be measured
- lack of accuracy, stability and durability of some types of sensor
- mismatch between what can be monitored and what is needed by service life models.

Knowledge transfer:

- potential specifiers do not know what is possible
- published literature is fragmented
- the field is complex and multi-disciplinary requiring expert guidance
- lack of independent advisors with wide expertise.

However, there is growing recognition by those involved in the management of concrete structures that it is important to identify deterioration early, determine its structural significance, and to monitor the structure so that a timely intervention is possible and more serious problems may be avoided. The main drivers for more widespread monitoring are:

- the growing/ageing stock of existing infrastructure
- increasing demands for more durable new infrastructure
- safety case production
- the need to manage infrastructure more proactively
- developments in monitoring technology (see Section 6.2).

6.2 TRENDS

Remote condition monitoring is an increasingly active field of research throughout the world. Rapid advances in sensor electronics and telecommunications technology over the past 20 years have opened up new opportunities for the remote monitoring of concrete structures. The clear trend is to smaller sensors, with wireless data transfer and real time computer analysis, that is, the provision of an integrated, stand-alone, intelligent remote monitoring system.

Fibre optic sensors are being increasingly used for monitoring, especially bridges, because of the advantages they offer over conventional strain gauge sensors, such as the ability to measure changes at various points along the fibre length (ie distributed sensing), immunity to electromagnetic interference, freedom from drift, the ability to measure strains at multiple orders (two or three) of magnitude better than conventional electrical resistance gauges, high shock resistance, and good durability. They are also easily incorporated into various types of measuring device (eg accelerometers, displacement transducers), and different physical quantities can be measured simultaneously with the appropriate system design and calibration.

Sensors are becoming smaller through new technological developments. MEMS are miniature electromechanical sensor and actuator systems that are capable of being optimised in their design for a specific application. They can be extremely small, down to micron size and with added circuitry they are still only millimetres in size. This small size allows them to be implemented in applications where conventional devices would be intrusive. An attraction of MEMS is that they can be used to both sense and actuate. The key difference between conventional sensing technologies and MEMS sensing technologies is in their intelligence capabilities, with the majority of MEMS devices containing an on-board microprocessor. The microprocessor can be typically used for digital processing, conversion from analogue to digital, performing basic calculations, and providing interface functions. This will ease the development of *smart infrastructure* that has attached or built-in components that can collect and transmit information about the state of the infrastructure to a central computer and receive back instruction from the computer, which actuates devices that adjust the state of the structure. For example, this could involve deflection or strain measurements on a bridge deck controlling the traffic lights allowing traffic onto the bridge, or controlling jacks applying forces to the deck.

Wired connections from sensors to computer, control or data logging terminals are rapidly changing in favour of wireless throughout many industrial sectors. Sensors are now available that include data logging and transmission capabilities. Wireless communication has particular advantages in civil engineering because of the size and remoteness of structures, the cost and damaging effects of installing wires, and the opportunity wireless offers for installing temporary sensors on structures or moving them cost effectively. Wireless communication includes radio frequency, cellular phone networks, and satellite links. High frequency transmission is used for short distances, with Bluetooth and Zigbee the most common protocols now available. The General Packet Radio Service (GPRS), a global system for mobile communications, provides users with packet data service over GSM radio channels and external packet data networks.

6.3 AREAS MERITING FURTHER WORK

Research is required to both improve sensor types available now and to develop new kinds of sensor. Key issues are accuracy, drift, calibration, robustness, and durability. There are more than fifty different types of sensor with scope for improvement in relation to long-term intelligent monitoring of concrete structures. Detailed critical feedback concerning the field performance of different sensor types is required.

Developments in other fields, for example relating to optical fibre distributed sensing, chemical sensing and MEMS need to be monitored and, where possible, exploited. There is scope for fruitful new collaborations between the scientists developing sensor science for other application domains and civil engineers. If possible, new sensors should take advantage of the development, of wireless, low power, smart sensor nodes.

There is a need for work on developing software architecture for analysing sensor data in real time.

The practical problems associated with the embedment of sensors in concrete structures are not encountered in most other application domains and require further research to establish the best strategies to avoid them. For example, embedment methods need to be developed so that the influence of the embedding/sealing material on the measured result is minimised and methods of detailing new structures to allow retro fitting of monitoring systems need to be developed. Research is also needed on energy scavenging in the built environment and on the transmission of radio waves through concrete so that the power needs for wireless sensors at different embedment depths can be established.

Considerable research effort is required to develop a comprehensive set of life prediction models capable of representing the complete behaviour of reinforced concrete elements subject to deterioration, based on monitoring data, with intervention strategies considered. Where possible these models should be based on automated monitoring of the chemical and physical changes occurring directly as a consequence of the degradation mechanism under consideration. In some cases, the associated monitoring methods will also have to be developed, so a concerted effort is needed to integrate the knowledge base and capabilities of the separate disciplines of automated monitoring and life prediction. There are many significant challenges that should be addressed and for which the way forward is far from clear. These include how best to model the effects of cracks, defects and other aspects of spatial variability, micro-environments, combinations of deterioration processes and life-extending treatments including surface treatments and corrosion inhibitors.

One area identified as being particularly worthy of research, having been largely overlooked to date, is measuring strain to monitor various types of deterioration. At present strain measurements are among the most reliable made and offer a relatively simple means of monitoring and modelling deterioration mechanisms resulting in expansion including rebar corrosion, sulphate attack, alkali aggregate reaction and freeze-thaw attack.

Dissemination and education are required to remove the mystery and uncertainty surrounding what is possible and how it may be accomplished, the objective being to encourage the appropriate application of intelligent monitoring. This CIRIA guide is a good start. Case studies reporting good practice need to be collated and disseminated. At present case studies rarely cover more than the system specified and its installation. To be of real value, case studies need to cover management issues including organisational procedures to ensure that the data is managed in a continuous way through the life of the system, problems, results, information on how the results were interpreted and used in any modelling and how these feed into an intervention strategy. Monitoring the built environment should be a module of undergraduate civil engineering degree courses and there is also scope for the introduction of a specialised MSc course on the subject.

7 References

ACI (2003)
"Non-destructive test methods for evaluation of concrete in structures"
Report ACI 228.2R-98, American Concrete Institute, Michigan, USA

ACI (2003)
Manual of concrete practice
American Concrete Institute. Available from: <www.concrete.org>

AL-SULAIMANI, G J, KALEEMULLAH, M, BASUNBUL, I A and RASHEEDUZZAFAR (1990)
"Influence of corrosion and cracking on bond behavior and strength of reinforced concrete members"
ACI Structural Journal, vol 87, pp 220–231

ANG, A H-S and TANG, W H (1984)
Probability concepts in engineering planning and design – vol. 2: Decision, risk and reliability
Wiley, Chichester (ISBN: 0-47103-201-8)

ASTM (2003)
Standard test method for resistance of concrete to rapid freezing and thawing
C666/C666M-03ASTM International

ASTM (1999)
Standard test method for half-cell potentials of uncoated reinforcing steel in concrete
WK3702 Revision of C876-91, ASTM, USA

ATKINSON, A and HEARNE, J A (1990)
"Mechanistic model for the durability of concrete barriers exposed to sulphate-bearing groundwater"
In: *Proc Materials Research Society Symposium*, vol 176, pp 149–156

AUYEUNG, Y, CHUNG, L and BALAGURU, P (2000)
"Bond behavior of corroded reinforcement bars"
ACI Materials Journal, vol 97, pp 214–220

AYLOTT, P, JOHN, G, ATHERTON, E and HASSANEIN, A (2003)
"The development of concrete and corrosion condition sensors for railway tunnels"
In: *Conf Corrosion/2003, NACE, San Diego, USA, 16–20 March*

BAILEY, T C and GATRELL, A C (1995)
Interactive spatial data analysis
Longman Scientific and Technical, Harlow (ISBN: 0-58224-493-5)

BAZANT, ZP (1979)
"Physical model for steel corrosion in concrete sea structures – application"
Journal of the Structural Division, ASCE, vol 105, pp 1155–1166

BAZANT, Z P and STEFFENS, A (2000)
"Mathematical model for kinetics of alkali-silica reaction in concrete"
Cement and Concrete Research, vol 30, pp 419–428

BHARGAVA, K, GHOSH, A K, MORI, Y and RAMANUJAM, S (2003)
"Analytical model of corrosion-induced cracking of concrete considering the stiffness of reinforcement"
Structural engineering and mechanics, vol 16, pp 749-769

BROOMFIELD, J, DAVIES, K, HLADKY, K and NOYCE, P (2003)
"Monitoring of reinforcement corrosion in concrete structures in the field"
In: *Proc Concrete Solutions, 1st int conf on concrete repair, St. Malo, Brittany, 15-17 July*

BUNGEY, J H and MILLARD, S G (1995)
Testing of concrete structures 3rd edition
Blackie Academic and Professional Publishers (ISBN: 978-0-75140-241-4)

CABRERA, J G and GHODDOUSSI, P (1992)
"The effect of reinforcement corrosion on the strength of the steel/concrete bond"
In: *Proc Int Conf on bond in concrete, Riga, Latvia,* pp 10/11–10/24

CAIRNS, J (1995)
"Strength in shear of concrete beams with exposed reinforcement"
In: *Proc the Institution of Civil Engineers, structures and buildings,* vol 110, pp 176–185

CAIRNS, J, PLIZZARI, G A, DU, Y, LAW, D W and FRANZONI, C (2005)
"Mechanical properties of corrosion-damaged reinforcement"
Materials Journal, ACI, vol 102, pp 256–264

CAIRNS, J and ZHAO, Z (1993)
"Behaviour of concrete beams with exposed reinforcement"
In: *Proc the Institution of Civil Engineers, structures and buildings*, vol 99, pp 141–154

CARDE, C, FRANCOIS, R and TORRENTI, J M (1996)
"Leaching of both calcium hydroxide and C-S-H from cement paste: modeling the mechanical behavior"
Cement and Concrete Research, vol 26, pp 1257–1268

CARSE, A and DUX, P F (1990)
"Measurement of concrete expansive strains due to alkali-silica reaction in Australian concrete structures"
Cement and Concrete Research, vol 20, pp 376-384

CHASE, S B and WASHER, G (1997)
"Nondestructive valuation for bridge management in the next century"
Public Roads, vol 61, pp 16–25, US Federal Highway Administration, Washington

CHO, N, KIM, N, JANG, J and CHANG, S (2000)
"Estimation of deflection curve of bridges using fiber optic strain sensors"
In: *Proc of SPIE (the International Society for Optical Engineering)*, vol 3988, pp 339–348

CLIMENT-LLORCA, M A, VIQUEIRA-PÉREZ, E and LÓPEZ-ATALAYA, M M (1996)
"Embeddable Ag/AgCl sensors for in-situ monitoring chloride contents in concrete"
Cement and Concrete Research, vol 26, **8**, pp 1157–1161

COHEN, M D, YIXIA, Z and DOLCH, W L (1992)
"Non-air-entrained high-strength concrete – is it frost resistant?"
Materials Journal, ACI, vol 89, 4, Jul-Aug, pp 406–415

CONCRETE SOCIETY (2000)
Diagnosis of deterioration in concrete structures – identification of defects, evaluation and development and remedial action
Technical Report No 54, Concrete Society, UK

CONCRETE BRIDGE DEVELOPMENT GROUP TG2 (2002)
Guide to testing and monitoring the durability of concrete structures
CBDG/008, Concrete Society, UK

CONTECVET (2001)
A validated users manual for assessing the residual service life of concrete structures
CD-ROM, British Cement Association, Crowthorne, Berkshire, UK

DIAMANTIDIS, D (2001)
Probabilistic assessment of existing structures
Joint Committee on Structural Safety (JCSS), RILEM Publications SARL

DURACRETE (2000)
Probabilistic performance based durability design of concrete structures
Brite EuRam III, Project BE95-1347, Document BE95-1347/R17

EL MAADDAWY, T, SOUDKI, K and TOPPER, T (2005)
"Analytical model to predict nonlinear flexural behavior of corroded reinforced concrete beams"
Structural Journal, ACI, vol 102, pp 550–559

ELSENER, B, ZIMMERMANN, L, FLÜCKIGER, D, BÜRCHLER, D and BÖHNI, H (1997)
"Non-destructive determination of the free chloride content in mortar and concrete"
In: *Proc RILEM int workshop*, L O Nilsson and J P Olivier (eds), RILEM pp 17–26

ENGELUND, S and SORENSEN, J D (1998)
"A probabilistic model for chloride-ingress and initiation of corrosion in reinforced concrete structures"
Structural Safety, vol 20, pp 69–89

ENRIGHT, M P and FRANGOPOL, D M (1998)
"Probabilistic analysis of resistance degradation of reinforced concrete bridge beams under corrosion"
Engineering Structures, vol 20, pp 960–971, Elsevier BV

ENRIGHT, M P and FRANGOPOL, D M (1999)
"Condition prediction of deteriorating concrete bridges using Bayesian updating"
Journal of Structural Engineering, vol 125, pp 1118–1125

EYRE, J R and NOKHASTEH, M A (1992)
"Strength assessment of corrosion damaged reinforced concrete slabs and beams"
In: *Proc the Institution of Civil Engineers, structures and buildings*, vol 94, pp 197–203

FAIRBAIRN, E M R, RIBEIRO, F L B, LOPES, L E, TOLEDO-FILHO, R D and SILVOSO, M M (2006)
"Modelling the structural behaviour of a dam affected by alkali-silica reaction"
Communications in numerical methods in engineering, Wiley, vol 22, pp 1–12

FAN, S H and HANSON, J M (1998)
"Effect of alkali silica reaction expansion and cracking on structural behavior of reinforced concrete beams"
Structural Journal, ACI, vol 95, pp 498–505

FARAGE, M C R, ALVES, J L D and FAIRBAIRN, E M R (2004)
"Macroscopic model of concrete subjected to alkali-aggregate reaction"
Cement and Concrete Research, Elsevier BV, vol 34, pp 495–505

GLASS, G K, HASSANEIN, N M and BUENFELD, N R (1997)
"Neural network modelling of chloride binding"
Magazine of Concrete Research, vol 49, pp 323–335

HAGA, K, SUTOU, S, HIRONAGA, M, TANAKA, S and NAGASAKI, S (2005)
"Effects of porosity on leaching of Ca from hardened ordinary Portland cement paste"
Cement and Concrete Research, Elsevier BV, vol 35, pp 1764–1775

HOFFMAN, P C and WEYERS, R E (1996)
"Probabilistic durability analysis of reinforced concrete bridge decks"
In: *Proc the Seventh Speciality Conference, Probabilistic Mechanics and Structural Reliability, Worcester, Massachusetts, 7–9 August, 1996*, (eds) Dan M. Frangopol and Mircea D. Grigoriu, ASCE, New York, pp 290–293

HORSZCZARUK, E (2004)
"The model of abrasive wear of concrete in hydraulic structures"
Wear, Technical University of Szczecin, Poland, vol 256, pp 787–96. Available from: <www.sciencedirect.com>

HUOVINEN, S (1993)
"Abrasion of concrete structures by ice"
Cement and Concrete Research, Elsevier BV, vol 23, pp 69–82

INAUDI, D, CASANOVA, N, VURPILLOT, S, GLISIC, B, KRONENEBERG, P and LLORET, S (2000)
Lessons learned in the use of fiber optic sensor for civil structural monitoring
In: *Proc conf The present and the future in health monitoring*, Weimar, Germany, Edifictio publisher, pp 79–92

ISGOR, O B and RAZAQPUR, A G (2004)
"Finite element modeling of coupled heat transfer, moisture transport and carbonation processes in concrete structures"
Cement and Concrete Composites, Elsevier, vol 26, 1, January, pp 57–73

ISTRUCTE (1992)
Structural effects of alkali-silica reaction. Technical guidance on the appraisal of existing structures
Institution of Structural Engineers. Available from: <www.istructe.org/publications>

JONES, A E K and CLARK, L A (1994)
"Practicalities and theory of using crack width summation to estimate ASR expansion"
In: *Proc the Institution of Civil Engineers, structures and buildings*, vol 104, pp 183-192

KARIMI, A R (2001)
Probabilistic assessment of deterioration and strength of concrete bridge beams and slabs
PhD Thesis, Department of Civil and Environmental Engineering, Imperial College of Science, Technology and Medicine, London, UK

KARIMI, A R and RAMACHANDRAN, K (1999)
"Probabilistic estimation of corrosion in bridges due to chlorination"
In: *Proc the ICASP 8 Conference: Application of Statistics and Probability, Sydney, Australia*, vol 2, pp 681–688

KARIMI, A R, RAMACHANDRAN, K, BUENFELD, N and CROWDER, M J (2005)
"Probabilistic analysis of reinforcement corrosion with spatial variability"
In: *Proc 9th Int conf on structural safety and reliability, ICOSSAR'05, Rome, Italy* (CD-Rom)

KHUNTHONGKEAW, J and TANGTERMSIRIKUL, S (2005)
"Model for simulating carbonation of fly ash concrete"
Journal of Materials in Civil Engineering, ASCE, vol 17, **5**, pp 570–578

KURTIS, K E, MONTEIRO, P J M and MADANAT, S M (2000)
"Empirical models to predict concrete expansion caused by sulfate attack"
Materials Journal, ACI, vol 97, pp 156–161

LAU, K-T (2003)
"Fibre-optic sensors and smart composites for concrete applications: A review article"
Magazine of Concrete Research, vol 55, **1**, pp 19–34

LEUNG, C K Y (2001)
Fiber optic sensors in concrete: The future?
NDT & E International, Elsevier BV, vol 34, **2**, pp 85–94

LI, C Q, LAWANWISUT, W and ZHENG, J J (2005)
"Time-dependent reliability method to assess the serviceability of corrosion-affected concrete structures"
Journal of Structural Engineering, vol 131, pp 1674–1680

LI, Y, VROUWENVELDER, T and WIJNANTS, G H (2003)
"Spatial variability of concrete degradation"
Life-cycle performance of deteriorating structures – assessment, design and management, American Society of Civil Engineers (ASCE), D M Frangopol, E Bruhwiler, M H Faber and B Adey (eds), pp 49–58

LIU, Y and WEYERS, R E (1998)
"Modeling the time-to-corrosion cracking in chloride contaminated reinforced concrete structures"
Materials Journal, ACI, vol 95, pp 675–681

LIU, W, HUNSPERGER, R, CHAJES, M, FOLLIARD, K and KUNZ, E (2002)
"Corrosion detection of steel cables using time domain reflectometry"
Journal of Materials in Civil Engineering, ASCE, vol 14, pp 217–223

MAINGUY, M and COUSSY, O (2000)
"Propagation fronts during calcium leaching and chloride penetration"
Journal of Engineering Mechanics, vol 126, pp 250–257

MANGAT, P S and ELGARF, M S (1999)
"Bond characteristics of corroding reinforcement in concrete beams"
Materials and structures (Materiaux et constructions), vol 32, pp 89–97

MARCHAND, J, SAMSON, E, MALTAIS, Y and BEAUDOIN, J J (2002)
"Theoretical analysis of the effect of weak sodium sulfate solutions on the durability of concrete"
Cement and Concrete Composites, Elsevier BV, vol 24, **3**, pp 317–329

MELCHERS, R E (1999)
Structural reliability analysis and prediction
John Wiley, Chichester (ISBN: 0-47198-324-1)

MOHAMMED, T U, HAMADA, H and YAMAJI, T (2003)
"Alkali-silica reaction-induced strains over concrete surface and steel bars in concrete"
Materials Journal, ACI, vol 100, pp 133–142

NGUYEN, V H, NEDJAR, B, COLINA, H and TORRENTI, J M (2006)
"A separation of scales homogenization analysis for the modelling of calcium leaching in concrete"
Computer methods in applied mechanics and engineering, Elsevier BV, vol 195, **52**, November, pp 7196–7210

NILSSON, L O, SANDBERG, P, POULSEN, E, TANG, L, ANDERSEN, A and FREDERIKSEN, J M (1997)
HETEK, a system for estimation of chloride ingress into concrete. Theoretical background
Report no 83, Road Directorate, Denmark Ministy of Transport. Available from: <www.hetek.teknologisk.dk>

OKADA T, KONISHI, S, MOHRI, T and TATEYAMA, K (2001)
"Detection of cracks on tunnel concrete linings with electric conductive paint"
In: *Proc Int symposium on modern tunneling science and technology, Kyoto, Japan*, pp 325–328

OUYANG, C, NANNI, A and CHANG, W F (1988)
"Internal and external sources of sulfate ions in Portland cement mortar: two types of chemical attack"
Cement and Concrete Research, Elsevier BV, vol 18, pp 69–709

PANTAZOPOULOU, S J and PAPOULIA, K D (2001)
"Modeling cover-cracking due to reinforcement corrosion in RC structures"
Journal of Engineering Mechanics, ASCE, vol 127, 4, April, pp 342-351

PENTTALA, V and AL-NESHAWY, F (2002)
"Stress and strain state of concrete during freezing and thawing cycles"
Cement and Concrete Research, Elsevier BV, vol 32, 9, September, pp 1407-1420

POWERS, T C (1945)
Working hypothesis for further studies of frost resistance of concrete
ACI Journal Proceedings, vol 41, **4**, February, pp 245–272

POWERS, T C (1949)
"The air requirements of frost-resistant concrete. Proceedings of the Highway Research Board"
In: *Proc Highway Research Board*, vol 29, pp 184–211, Bulletin no 33, Research and Developments Laboratories, Portland Cement Association

RAFIQ, M I, CHRYSSANTHOPOULOS, M K and ONOUFRIOU, T (2004A)
"Performance updating of concrete bridges using proactive health monitoring methods"
Reliability Engineering & System Safety, Elsevier BV, vol 86, **3**, December, pp 247–256

RAFIQ, M I, CHRYSSANTHOPOULOS, M K and ONOUFRIOU, T (2004B)
"Sensitivity analysis of chloride induced deterioration in concrete bridges"
In: *Proc 2nd int conf on bridge maintenance, safety and management, IABMAS'04, Kyoto, Japan* (CD-Rom)

RAOOF, M and LIN, Z (1997)
"Structural characteristics of RC beams with exposed main steel"
Structures and buildings, Institution of Civil Engineers, vol 122, February, pp 35–51

RAUPACH, M and SCHIESSL, P (2001)
"Macrocell sensor systems for monitoring of the corrosion risk of the reinforcement in concrete structures"
NDT and E International, Elseveier BV, vol 34, **6**, September, pp 435–442(8)

SAETTA, A V, SCHREFLER, B A and VITALIANI, R V (1993)
"Carbonation of concrete and the mechanism of moisture, heat and carbon dioxide flow through porous materials"
Cement and Concrete Research, vol 23, pp 761–772

SARJA, A and VESIKARI, E (1996)
Durability design of concrete structures
Report of RILEM Technical Committee 130-CSL, Spon, London (ISBN: 0-41921-410-0)

STANISH, K, HOOTON, R D and PANTAZOPOULOU, S J (1999)
"Corrosion effects on bond strength in reinforced concrete"
ACI Structural Journal, vol 96, pp 915–921

STEWART, M G and ROSOWSKY, D V (1998)
"Structural safety and serviceability of concrete bridges subject to corrosion"
Journal of Infrastructure Systems, vol 4, **4**, December, pp 146–155

STEWART, M G, FABER, M H and GEHLEN, C (2003)
"Temporal and spatial aspects of probabilistic corrosion models"
In: *Proc to the Joint JCSS, fib and LCC03 workshop at EPFL, Lausanne, Switzerland, March 24-26 2003*, pp 183–193. *Life-cycle performance of deteriorating structures; Assessment, design and management*, D M Frangopol et al (eds) ASCE (2004) (ISBN: 0-78440-707-X)

TANG, L (1996)
Chloride transport in concrete – Measurement and prediction
Publication P-96:6, Department of Buildings Materials, Chalmers University of Technology, Goteborg, Sweden

THOFT-CHRISTENSEN, P and BAKER, M J (1982)
Structural reliability theory and its applications
Springer-Verlag, Berlin, New York (ISBN: 0-38711-731-8)

THOFT-CHRISTENSEN, P, JENSEN, F M, MIDDLETON, C R and BLACKMORE, A (1997)
"Revised rules for concrete bridges"
Safety of bridges, P C Das (ed), Thomas Telford Publishing, pp 175–188

THOMAS, M D A and BENTZ, E C (2000)
Life-365: Computer program for predicting the service life and life-cycle costs of reinforced concrete exposed to chlorides
American Concrete Institute, Detroit, MI, USA

TIXIER, R and MOBASHER, B (2003)
"Modeling of damage in cement-based materials subjected to external sulfate attack. I: formulation"
Journal of Materials in Civil Engineering, vol 15, **4**, July/August, pp 305–313

ULM, F J, COUSSY, O, KEFEI, L and LARIVE, C (2000)
"Thermo-chemo-mechanics of ASR expansion in concrete structures"
Journal of Engineering Mechanics, vol 126, **3**, March, pp 233–242

ULM, F J, TORRENTI, J M and ADENOT, F (1999)
"Chemoporoplasticity of calcium leaching in concrete"
Journal of Engineering Mechanics, vol 125, 10, pp 1200–1211

VANMARCKE, E (1983)
Random fields: Analysis and synthesis
MIT Press, Cambridge, MA (ISBN: 0-26222-026-1)

VU, K A T and STEWART, M G (2000)
"Structural reliability of concrete bridges including improved chloride-induced corrosion models"
Structural Safety, Elsevier BV, vol 22, **4**, pp 313-333

VU, K A T and STEWART, M G (2001)
"Cracking and spalling reliability analysis considering spatial variability for reinforced concrete structures"
In: *Proc 8th Int conf on structural safety and reliability, ICOSSAR'01, R B Corotis, G I Schueller and M Shinozuka (eds)*, A A Balkema, Rotterdam (CD-Rom)

VU, K A T and STEWART, M G (2005)
"Predicting the likelihood and extent of reinforced concrete corrosion-induced cracking"
Journal of Structural Engineering, vol 131, **11**, November, pp 1681–1689

VU, K A T, STEWART, M G and MULLARD, J (2005)
"Corrosion-induced cracking: experimental data and predictive models"
ACI Structural Journal, vol 102, **5**, September, pp 719–726

WANG, X and LIU, X (2004)
"Bond strength modeling for corroded reinforcement in reinforced concrete"
Structural Engineering and Mechanics, vol 17, pp 863–878

WILLIAMSON, S J and CLARK, L A (2002)
"Effect of corrosion and load on reinforcement bond strength"
Structural Engineering International, International Association for Bridge and Structural Engineering, vol 12, **2**, 1 May, pp 117–122

Summary

Management of concrete structures requires an understanding of the deterioration processes involved and the rate at which they proceed. Intelligent monitoring is automated monitoring which explicitly provides information on current condition and deterioration rates to assist in predicting the remaining life of a component or structure. Surface mounted or embedded sensors may be used to monitor various aspects of structural condition, reinforcement corrosion, and the environment in and around a concrete structure.

Intelligent monitoring of concrete structures

Buenfeld NR, Davies RD, Karimi A, Gilbertson A L

CIRIA

CIRIA C661 © CIRIA 2008 CON120 ISBN: 978-0-86017-661-9

British Library Cataloguing in Publication Data

A catalogue record for this book is available from the British Library

Keywords

Building technology, concrete and structures, facilities management, *in situ* testing and instrumentation, materials, materials technology

Reader interest	Classification	
Reinforced concrete, concrete structures, monitoring, whole-life, life-prediction, instrumentation, durability, structural health monitoring, management of structures	Availability	Unrestricted
	Content	Design and management guidance
	Status	Committee-guided
	USER	Reinforced concrete designers and specifiers, construction planners and engineers, concrete technologists, managers of structures, instrumentation engineers and suppliers

Published by CIRIA, Classic House, 174-180 Old Street, London EC1V 9BP, UK

CIRIA C661

London, 2008

sharing knowledge ▪ building best practice

Classic House, 174–180 Old Street, London EC1V 9BP
TELEPHONE 020 7549 3300 FAX 020 7253 0523
EMAIL enquiries@ciria.org
WEBSITE www.ciria.org